Unravel Dis-ease]

Discover just how amazing your Mind, Body and Spirit is

By
Catherine Rolt

Photo by Robin Feild www.impromptuphotography.co.uk

Illustrations by Min Cooper www.fieldrowgallery.co.uk/
Min@MinCooperPrints

To the three, mostly, unsung heroes in my life during the last years

Andrew Baker for sharing your home so generously and then cherishing me through so much surgery. You have always believed in me, and constantly reminded me in your wonderful way "that eventually the wheel would turn". You have been amazing, loyal and steadfast in so many remarkable ways. I have fried your circuits so often, and yet you have never wavered from supporting me, providing a stable base while my own physical structure was being rebuilt and then re-calibrated. Thank you Lord Smidgen.

Toby Rolt, for being the best brother that anyone could hope to have. You make me laugh continuously. After an absence of almost 36 years in each other's lives, I treasure every single moment of you back in my days. You have been so brave throughout all of this, always living with all the knowledge of how perilous and dangerous my days can be on multiple levels, whilst all along looking so well. You are endlessly fighting my corner and facing my reality. Thank you for having my back with your knowing, great wisdom and thoughtfulness. You are so hugely talented and a remarkable person to have as my brother.

Vast thanks go to Chris P for being there through all this in unsaid ways that endlessly saved my bacon. I shall always be grateful for your insights, wisdom and generosity. Thank you also for giving me such valuable information for this book.

Also this is dedicated to all the medical Zebras. (Medical Definition of ZEBRA - It comes from an old saying used in teaching medical students about how to think logically in regard to the differential diagnosis: 'When you hear hoofbeats think of horses, not zebras.')

To all those who bravely live with any of, or even all of these:-
Ehlers-Danlos Syndrome,
Postural Orthostatic Tachycardia Syndrome
Mast Cell Activation Disorder

A brief explanation of these syndromes is on Page 11

Although, mostly, we are conundrums to the medical world, we are also the pioneers that will help the next generations have much more support, care and expertise available than we have known. We have connective tissue disorders and yet the paradox is that we are some of the most connecting people I know. I hope and pray that we use our connecting skills to keep making the suffering far less for the next generations, as well as ourselves. We are a powerful force and can make the breakthroughs that are necessary.

Foreward by Ann Wilson – author of "The Wealth Chef"

"We must go beyond textbooks, go out into the bypaths and untrodden depths of the wilderness and travel and explore and tell the world the glories of our journey."

This is the sage advice of John Hope Franklin and it is exactly what Catherine Rolt has done.

The wilderness is where life is most intensely, exquisitely and excruciatingly felt.

It is in these wild extreme places, far away from the everyday comforts, that the layers of externally defined worthiness and identity we all get caught up in, are outed for their utter uselessness and drop away, revealing the truth

> You have to go into the wilderness to discover this truth.

> The truth that you are already worthy.

> The truth that you are already enough.

> The truth that there is nothing you can do or have or be or experience that can change your intrinsic worthiness.

> The truth that nothing outside of your raw life essence means a damn thing!

But going into the wilderness on our own to connect with this deep knowing can be a seriously daunting and terrifying task.

Having a guide with vast experience of living past the edge, a guide who is willing to show you how to navigate the wilderness and not only survive but thrive is priceless.

When we find such a guide we should follow.

Catherine Rolt is one of the greatest wilderness guides I have ever met and I feel deeply grateful she came into my life and shared with me some of the wild places she has travelled to and lived in.

Catherine's wilderness is not the African bush, the Alaskan tundra, or the vast open oceans. Catherine's wilderness is the places she has experienced as a result of a life lived at the extreme of a body riddled with complex physical challenges and pain. The wild places she has traversed as she's been brought back to life over nine times, and endured 35 complex surgeries.

Catherine's journeys into the wilderness have given her incredible insight as to what life really is and its paradox.

She knows we are not our bodies yet we need our bodies to experience life.

She knows our worthiness is not defined by our net worth yet we need money and material things to support life.

Catherine's deep and profound journey is really an exquisite love story – a story of falling deeply in love with life.

During her travels in the wilderness she discovered the most wonderful things.

She discovered herself.

She discovered the real essence of life and a life well lived.

She learned how to direct and utilise the resources of the

physical world in support of life's expression but never to define it.

She discovered the path to healing and vibrant energetic health.

Thank you Catherine for sharing the glories of your travels with us.

CONTENTS

INTRODUCTION..13
Unravel Dis-ease Naturally

Discover your Large Intestine...25
Chapter 1
Nature will always show the way

Discover your Lungs 45
Chapter 2
Inner knowledge is the key to your outer wealth, no matter what!

Discover your Kidneys...73
Chapter 3
L'addition, s'il vous plait (The Bill please.)

Discover your bladder 99
Chapter 4
Burdens Of Carelessness

Discover your Gallbladder..123
Chapter 5
Beyond A Place Where There Is No Hope - Gallbladder

Discover your Liver 151
Chapter 6
Sexuality becomes integrated with our Spirituality

Discover our Triple Burner 177
Chapter 7
Laughing With Self, Lightly Tossed - Triple Burner / Thermostat

Discover your Small intestine 203

Chapter 8

    Your internal committee and boardroom

Discover your Heart..**223**
Chapter 9

    "Spiritual Spinning" or "Topping and Tailing"

Discover your Pericardium...**245**
Chapter 10

    Humour Is Perhaps God's Grace In Action

Discover your Stomach...**261**
Chapter 11

    Kickbacks every time we go forward

Discover your Spleen..**295**
Chapter 12

    The divine in all things, very particularly the seemingly unforgivable

Chapter 13 ....**311**

    Conclusion - My silver thread

Brief description of the three main syndromes:

Ehlers-Danlos syndrome (EDS) is a group of genetic tissue disorders. Although signs vary hugely according to what type of EDS the person has, typically the joints, skin, blood vessels are affected and there are effects ranging from mildly loose joints to life-threatening complications.   Major signs and symptoms are listed below.

Musculoskeletal

Musculoskeletal symptoms include hyper flexible joints that are unstable and prone to sprain, dislocation, subluxation, and hyperextension. There can be an early onset of advanced osteoarthritis, chronic degenerative joint disease, swan-neck deformity of the fingers, and Boutonniere deformity of the fingers. Tearing of tendons or muscles may occur. Deformities of the spine, such as scoliosis (curvature of the spine), kyphosis (a thoracic hump), tethered spinal cord syndrome, and occipitoatlantoaxial hypermobility may also be present. There can also be myalgia (muscle pain) and arthralgia (joint pain), which may be severe and disabling. Trendelenburg's sign is often seen, which means that when standing on one leg, the pelvis drops on the other side. Osgood–Schlatter disease, a painful lump on the knee, is common as well. In infants, walking can be delayed (beyond 18 months of age), and bottom-shuffling instead of crawling occurs.

Mast cell activation syndrome (MCAS) is one type of mast cell activation disorder (MCAD), and is an immunological condition in which mast cells inappropriately and excessively release chemical mediators, resulting in a range of chronic symptoms, sometimes including anaphylaxis or near-anaphylaxis attacks. Primary symptoms include cardiovascular, dermatological, gastrointestinal, neurological and respiratory problems.

MCAS is still a poorly understood condition and is a current topic of research.

MCAS is often found in patients with Ehlers–Danlos syndrome (EDS) and postural orthostatic tachycardia syndrome (POTS). It is also found in subset groups of patients with common variable immunodeficiency (CVID).

Postural orthostatic tachycardia syndrome (POTS) is a condition in which a change from lying to standing causes an abnormally large increase in heart rate, with a startling drop in blood pressure. This occurs with symptoms that may include light-headedness, trouble thinking, blurry vision, or weakness. When my blood pressure drops I struggle to form sentences which makes people saying how 'articulate 'I am a joke!

INTRODUCTION

Unravel Dis-ease Naturally
Find out how amazing your mind, body and Spirit is

"So, what is the prognosis?"

I managed a reply, through a haze of unmanaged agonies, shortly after further life saving surgery. "Surgeries and re-welding the scaffolding which holds me together for the rest of my life"

I have never had to make any decisions about the surgeries, which in some respects has been a huge relief. My life was always suddenly in danger.

Sharply, and with greater authority seemingly than one of the finest surgeons in the world, came the response, "Oh no, it's quite wrong. You will have learnt your lessons by then."

When you have my particular life, along with countless others, who live with all sorts of complications, to have life presented as a series of lessons is not the full, even remotely helpful, picture. After all my integrated health opportunities and a career working with patients using Integrated Chinese Medicine, I have found ways around, through and in the midst of the challenges that do happen to all of us.

To a greater or lesser degree, there is not one single human that has not had heartbreak or emotional, physical and spiritual challenges. Of course though, life itself keeps happening. The seasons of Nature keep going. Energy keeps moving. We breathe in and then we let go.

Although, as this book shares, living our lives through the actual realities, which we can influence hugely, does bring about a passionate connection to what life can be.

What on earth does that mean?

Is it a total contradiction to also be living alongside a very rare type of an already unusual condition since my birth? This year I will be 57 years old and yet so far my life has been punctuated with :-

- 35 mostly emergency spinal/structural rebuilding operations, gynecological, digestive or cancer related surgeries.

- I have been re-built so much and so many times that my neck, spine, pelvis and hip look like a giant Meccano set which would not look out of place in a Star Wars movie.

- Almost totally deaf for the first seven years of my life until the first surgical intervention gave me back the gift of sounds. Boy were they loud too after only ever knowing blissful, to me, mostly silence.

- Three different cancer diagnoses, a close fourth, seemingly only months ago, as I wrote this book, requiring more and immediate further surgery.

- A stroke, narrowly escaping a second one.

- Endless infections and viral overloads nearly continuously as my body combats persistent chronic inflammation.

- MORE, so-called, official labels of diseases or conditions that have most medics scurrying towards the door and/or drinks cabinet fast.

- Had my life saved well over nine times.

- Gone way beyond my sell by date with apparently all of the above, living outside of any so called comfort zone on all levels.

Is health devoid of the continuous conflicts that actually make up all of our lives? Does the continual flow of our own energy systems mean that static health even exists? Life is actually about transforming through differing stages of dis-ease.

I, and many others in our world, spend each day tackling a host of health problems. It has been a lifelong journey of mine to understand my mind, body, and soul in order to cope with a rare genetic disorder and then to help others as well. After 9 years of training as an Integrated Chinese Medical practitioner a lot of the missing strands of necessary information have come together. Using this knowledge and all the other training I have done over the last 40 years, has enabled me to always find my way back to thriving and vibrant health, through all of the surgeries and much more.

This book is fundamentally about all the seeming, conflicting, contradictions in our lives – and yet, it is also about what is always right with us.

We will discover what vibrant and engaged, energetic integrated health within us actually is, and with the realities that we all have going on in our lives.

Unravel Dis-ease Naturally is sharing with you, our own inbuilt navigational systems that are constantly working within us.

We are living with so many belief systems around our health, our lives and outside circumstances that keep us shunted off our own amazing internal truths.

Each chapter of this book takes you through your own deeply connected associations to the seasons in nature.

We live with pitches in our tone of voices and our energy system that resonates either towards vibrant health or towards stagnant and muddied conflicted frequencies.

Whether we know it or not, our own energy systems are constantly interacting with everything around us. So the more we can awaken to that within us the more precious our every breath becomes.

This book is going to ask you to suspend what you think you know, then to come on a journey discovering how truly phenomenal our being is. The word "being" is used, as it makes up your integrated self. I will begin to show you how each season of our year is automatically taking us through externally what does in fact go on inside of us. There are colours, sounds and even smells that can be and are associated with organs within our bodies that have a continued flow of an internal journey going on. I am introducing you to your own phenomenal systems that are serving us all of the time.

In a mind, body and spirit, that are never separated, you will find out how much more hope and brilliance there is going on in even the most appalling of circumstances.

Within every single particle and atom that we are made up of, there is a code of integrated health, with it being possible to influence rogue cells. They are a warning system to us that we can become aware of and pay attention to. The energy systems and teachings within all religions is at their core showing us to master that coding. Each and every single event that happens is an integrated invitation to unravel that code for ourselves. The biblical phrase, "the truth will set you free", is a deep-seated vibration within our own DNA.

When I started training in Taoism / Chinese Medicine, it was astounding to have so much of life interconnected, which intuitively was such a breath of fresh air. Organs in our bodies were described in ways that were way beyond anything that had ever come near my limited education. The combination of wisdom, philosophy, quantum physics and thousands of years of experience of the laws of nature makes up Taoism. We were taught that Nature, and its rhythms, are functioning in us all, constantly. The more we get to master the natural rhythms within our own mind, body and spirit, the more we become masters of our own destinies, and souls purposes.

To make peace with life itself, it is vital to really begin to know yourself in an integrated way. Your body, your mind and your spirit is the combination of the greatest friend you will ever have.

Vibrant energetic health is never the absence of problems, signs and symptoms; it is literally how we are engaging with our life force, and the way we are translating the endless feedback mechanism that is the process of our life force.

In each chapter of this book, we journey through our organs' energy systems. There are stories and examples from working with patients and clients over the years that are real but have all been changed so that no one's identity is revealed. I also share my own personal stories, along with those of my mother.

Have you ever noticed that some of the happiest, most energetically alive people you know are not devoid of issues, problems and pain?

The following is how in Integrated Chinese Medicine we are trained to see the causes of disease. It is vital to understand that it is the suppression, and then as a result, the extremes of emotional states that lead to so many problems with our health. Equally how we are able to respond to the extremes in others' lives.

CAUSES OF DIS-EASE INTERNALLY AND EXTERNALLY

Internal causes

Anger
Joy
Worry
Over-thinking
Grief
Fear
Shock

External Causes

Wind
Cold
Damp
Summer Heat
Dryness
Fire
Damp Heat

Miscellaneous Causes

Constitution - genes
Overwork and fatigue
Exercise
Diet
Sex
Trauma
Parasites, poisons, fungus and bacteria
Inappropriate treatments

Secondary Causes

Blood stagnation
Phlegm

Additionally I would also be paying attention to the following during a consultation

- Dental treatments.

- Structural misalignments

- Electro magnetic resonance to close to the patient's head, heart or where they sleep.

- Contaminated foods that no longer resemble the fresh food from having just been recently harvested.

- Lack of fresh air.

- Noise pollution.

- What we are feeding our minds and senses in the form of external stimulation. (It has been discovered that the sound resonance of Hertz 432 is healing, rather than the considered normal of Hertz 440.)

- Insufficient sleep and real rest.

- Environmental pollution.

I would also add, having worked for so long with people, illness and dis-ease, that there are four other causes of sickness that is not often talked about. It is very relevant in clinical practise:

- Some people are seemingly carriers of other's unacknowledged pains and energetic imbalances.

- There are also situations of illness that I have now come to recognise as part of a bigger life purpose. I could write a whole book about this subject and what I have now experienced too often with a few but exceptional patients. What they suffer is almost an act of nothing else but service to others. Things are never quite as they seem in the world of dis-ease. I was first introduced to this idea while training with Neale Donald Walsh, who has written the series of books Conversations with God.

- Family dynamics can be a toxic ticking time bomb. Unresolved issues, resentments and shame, long and deeply buried in the core of family life can also be a huge factor in unravelling dis-ease. So often the unsaid dynamics are like bindweed throttling the energetic resources of family members.

- The synergy between health and wealth, both internal and external, is hugely relevant to clinical practise. To support ourselves and others in financial freedom will always be a very necessary factor in finding relief from underlying anxiety and worry. To unravel poverty beliefs that have become so entrenched is a must if vibrant health is to become a daily experience. Especially in the presence of a serious illness being negotiated daily.

All of these, inevitably, impact hugely on our sense of wellbeing on all levels, and very often a patient will have a few of these categories contributing to a sense of dis-ease. Therefore needing attention.

Aikido is a Japanese martial art which uses the motion/energy of the attacker, rather than opposing it head on. One of the gifts of having been born with this matrix blip is that it has given me the opportunity to harness what comes at me and not to oppose it, which would result in me experiencing more struggle and pain than I already do. I have to become very familiar with what I fondly know now as Spiritual Kung Fu or more accurately Spirit Aikido.

We are all in a grand gym of life, and in my case my life's purpose is needing and collecting experiences all around, mastering being incredibly well, whilst in fact I am very ill. The real paradox of life is exactly that. What are you up to, in the grandest scheme that you are able to imagine, sense, hear, feel and experience? If nothing was a mistake and if every single sign, symptom and so called problem that you have was actually just equipment in your own gym of life, wouldn't that already make a difference? Your own equipment bleeping at you?

We are all constantly bumping up against others who are extravagantly wealthy in some areas of their lives and then shockingly bankrupt in others. Then, there are others who are middling right across the board. Each of us has three main energetic bank accounts with our essence and purpose determining what is needed in each account to achieve just that. When we suddenly realise that we really have not got the control that we at first perhaps thought, and as suffering comes to the surface over some situation, then begins, in some senses, the real work of our lives. If we are not in the awakening state of dancing with our own life force then our energy is usually demanding our attention to be refocused. The ever changing state of our own individual balance needs us to get to know ourselves. So in the absence of most of us having a clue *"who"* we are, we remain, often, out of step with our own life force and energy bank.

To be in step with our life force, which very few of us really are, means that our own navigational system within us will find a way to help bring about the balance. So, when what we call a healing crisis arrives, we are forced into choices as to how we conduct what is now obviously so out of control and unmanageable. A massive decluttering has to then take place as we begin to realise that what we believed was relevant to our lives actually is not.

So, as our pain gets deeper and goes on long enough from the internal or external imbalances, the average person will find themselves having to find deeper tools to cope. In some ways that is the purpose of the endless rhythms of change and movement. We are propelled more and more into discovering what already is within, and without. Then, if at all possible, we find ways to transform what IS possible.

After all the surgeries and endless interventions and as I still am in the early stages of recovering from the last five structural rebuilds, I am also resoundingly the healthiest I have ever been. So you too can bring all of your issues, concerns and take what might allow you a different and gentler, kinder perspective on your own precious life.

Life is a constant paradox. To understand that, begins a dance which, in and of itself, sets your spirit free. Your purpose then comes to light with the increasing self-love and self-respect, which can become an automatic step in the daily dance.

You will begin to see and know your body and its organs in ways that you never would have imagined was possible. You will hopefully be freed from the bullying tyranny of thinking that there is endlessly something wrong with you, rather than actually you are just in a constant fantastic dance with your own life force. The more you get to know your engine, your vehicle, then the more choice you really have over your internal bank accounts, let alone your external ones.

As our natural resources are used up, for example rainforests, we are not taught to connect our behaviours with what is collectively happening in our world. Trees take in carbon dioxide and replace it with oxygen so they are nature's lungs. We are not able to unite with our common humanity, drop our self-importance and become more focused on solutions that are plentiful, but not easy for more than just some. We can remain in denial of the issues all around us, and truly believe that it is someone else's problem. Or we become so overwhelmed and frightened by discovering the part that we do play in plastic consumption, that we are overwhelmed.

When we live from more of our integrated health though we then, in turn, model real vibrant health to the world at large, as well as our cells – cells that recognise the flowing energy of the life force vibrantly moving with life, and not against.

Unravel Dis-ease takes you through the five seasons with the functions and organs associated with each. Four seasons have two functions and organs and the fifth season has four functions and two recognised organs from the Western Perspective. I have introduced the behaviour connected to these seasons and functions, whilst also introducing you to the idea of how much more everything is interconnected.

At the end of each chapter in this book, I list simple, not necessarily easy, tips for vibrant living – what I refer to as, "Unglamorous tips for glamorous living and tantalising teasers."

Of course each chapter is a small summary of such a vast and dynamically different way of embracing and seeing, hearing and feeling the integrated nature of everything.

Implement one of these changes at a time; allow yourself the feedback that your own body is going to start giving you.

Treat your own body like you would a new love affair. Be diligent, careful and thorough, taking nothing for granted. If you want a great lover and companion, it is worth the wait and patience involved in really sussing out if someone is right for you, in the same way it is the most important project of self-love that you will ever do – you are getting to know your own body.

Come with me as we make the connections to ourselves and to our world at large, and enjoy the health and wealth that is a natural overflow of being in harmony within ourselves and with Nature herself.

Chapter 1

Discover your

Large intestine

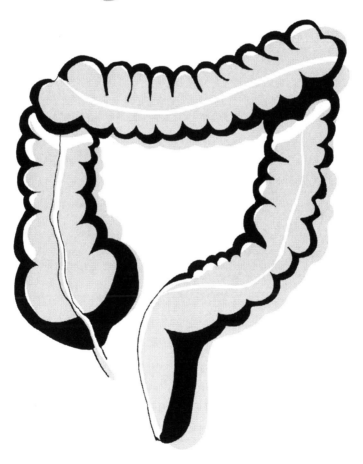

Nature will always show the way

Discover your Large Intestine.

Emotionally allowing for grief-sadness

Taking in the richness of life

The large intestine: drains the rubbish that cannot be utilised.

The large intestine: drains the rubbish that cannot be utilised.

As I lay in bed after spinal, neck, hip and pelvis surgeries, totting up the numbers of mostly spinal surgeries that I have had so far, I seriously wondered if I had it in me to get up at all. Thirty-five major surgeries seemed excessive to say the least. Having also had one stroke I did not want another. I knew damn well that my life had been extraordinary by anyone's imagination. Inevitably I reviewed my life and wondered what I could glean from how I had got up again and again previously. This time was different in that I was way too battered on all levels and no longer had my own home. My career, reliant on my physicality, seemed irreversibly in jeopardy. My greatest friends had hit their limits with the continual consequences of me being so ill, and walked out of my daily life, whilst others had died.

I was in acute and chronic isolation daily, living with a friend who had chivalrously offered me his home, for a few months. I knew no one and felt unhappier than I had known for years. Day after day I faced rebuilding every single aspect of every part of me through a haze of shock, grief and waves of despair and hopelessness, as well as exhaustion and pain. Every aspect of my new surroundings seemed to haunt me with being exactly what I would not wholeheartedly have chosen for myself. Gratefully and in constant conflict, though

26

I knew that the alternative had come hauntingly close to being in a bed and breakfast, courtesy of the housing benefits office. The few months had turned into an increasingly extended time that was rapidly turning into years of my life, and that with each passing month, seemed as if the life, that I had already fought so hard to have had, was gone, slipping away beyond my reach to regain. This was the ninth time that I was rebuilding a life and myself.

Vividly I remember thinking that I needed to treat myself like a new patient's visit, putting all the cards on the table. I made myself be detached from my realities, as I pretended to be my new practitioner supporting me through to solutions. Using the full extent of my imagination and creativity, I invited my life force back.

Two surgeons and their teams had done their bit. I now needed to do mine.

So what on earth were the ingredients from the past that I could re-enact? Oddly my almost total deafness of 7 years, and sense of baffling isolation as a child returned to me in that I retreated inside to my deepest place of solace.

I slowly saw a pattern emerging as I inevitably searched for clues to find a way of reconnecting to life. Over and through each surgical rebuild every single aspect of my life was always turned inside out as well as upside down. I would be catapulted into shifts internally that the surgery required. So returning to any of my previous life would mean a series of painful losses with bewildering mismatches. Mismatches in all of my interactions as I was recovering again and again. The journey back to some semblance of myself after such massive rebuilds was an hourly stretch through endless grief. The functioning of our organs in the autumn energy within us is deeply connected to our ability to grieve, to the taking in of the richness of life. When in balance it allows us to accept when something is over, to complete with the loss's involved and then be able to let go.

The problem, as I was able to diagnose, was that I was drowning in not having a clue how to get up, and what to grieve, with any richness of life having disappeared totally. No medicine, test or procedure was going to be able to help me do the internal work to get back up again.

As a student learning the skills of Integrated Chinese Medicine I was fascinated by my favourite teacher describing clinical practise as being 'energetic accounting', meaning that most dis-ease was about one or more of our internal accounts being over or under spent. Every which way our energy, body, mind and spirit was taught as if we were looking at energy-spread sheets of our past, present and future.

Being in such a state of physical, emotional and spiritual bankruptcy I knew I needed to align myself with life's possibilities. Merely surviving this all was not an option for the personality I have. I had to get back somehow to thriving again, and flourishing accounts.

The large intestine, which was always affected by the surgeries, infections and huge quantities of drugs had to be rebuilt on the physical, as well as emotional and spiritual level. The muscles in my stomach were cut straight through with some scar tissue pulling on the large intestine keeping it in tight spasm in places. A year of extremely strong antibiotics had blown any balance of the intestinal flora also.

It is difficult to take on board at first that the functions of our organs are part of an incredibly sophisticated system that is actually performing so many multi-levelled tasks for us.

In the West we tend to think of our physical bodies as just that. So a large intestine, our bowel is thought of just in terms of having bowel movements, or not. We do not generally have a clue that our bowel is also helping us to feel and be connected to the world, to take in the richness of life, to accept when something is over. It also gives us the ability to find inspiration and meaning. So as we let go of our stools we are endlessly preparing for the continuation of the natural cycle.

So in my case I have literally every few years had to reconstruct everything in my life, all my accounts on all levels. How on earth, I wondered, was I to find meaning again and reconnect to anything that seemed inspiring?

The losses involved are always vast and on-going with every single lifesaving emergency operation. For instance, new or budding relationships often did not make the leap of even literally the ocean, from the UK to America. Some of the surgeries were done in the States. The father of a man that was very keen on me was taken aside, for instance and told:

"You cannot marry this woman. She will be paralysed and will not give you children".

My clinics, which I ran simultaneously, had to be let go of with all of the dearly loved and respected patients, being transferred over to another practitioner. My finances would be torn asunder time and time again, whilst I was unable to earn any money during the long recoveries. I would be put in body casts for extended times, which would involve more loss of independence, and obviously mobility. The alternatives were, of course, something that I to this day am extremely grateful to have not experienced.

But, and it is a very big but, being grateful did not help me bypass the claustrophobic sensation of my independence being taken away, almost overnight as the surgeries were always gigantic emergencies, so there was never time to mull anything over.

Part of the recoveries was to find meaning again, and to experience the richness of life.

Imagine trees or flowers not being able to let go of dead leaves, ready for the next and new growth in the following season. In a similar fashion there was always a point when I would have to willingly let go of all that was dead to me. As the physical literal functioning of my bowel began working again I too would need to find a way through the losses.

As each spinal procedure takes the body about three years of painstaking adjustments, to have had five in such quick succession, was pushing me way beyond anything I trusted I could come back from, initially.

With every single twist and turn of fundamentally ill health I knew though that I had ended up somehow becoming more and more vibrantly alive, passionately engaged and connected to another layer of all that is integrated in nature.

Here are three examples of the Autumn season within us playing out in people's lives. When I was growing up, I had the privilege of knowing a stunningly beautiful woman, radiant inside and out. She had a healing practise with a genuine gift of being able to release suffering. I would see clients arriving dragging their deep terrible burdens of pain. They would go in to her peaceful, light-filled treatment space, burdened by dark clouds of menace twirling around them, or so it seemed to my sensitive intuition. Always, if at all possible, I would try to make sure that I was at the window to see the same clients leave. It brought such a blast of hope and sunshine into my own being when I saw them leave, as always they would come out, as if bathed in golden light, smiling with a spring in their step with no clouds around. I now understand that this gentle woman of the light and of the Angelic world would have connected them to their own heavens and gems, with their ability to let go having been witnessed. Her metal element within her was very strong and in very acute balance for her integrated purpose.

Virtually no one knew that this walking and almost literal Angel, masquerading as human, was suffering herself with crippling pain all day and all night. No one was able to resolve her pain; equally, no consultant understood why she was still alive at all. She downloaded what we call heavenly energy to live with, sharing it also with others. In her appearance and her demeanour, she vibrated with health and warmth, so that it simply was not possible for even one second to know that she was not completely well. Even though she had a walking stick no one ever saw it as they were knocked out by the light all around her. Radiance and vitality poured from her. She was my first real experience of someone truly living and thriving with illness and pain, with the real paradox of life.

I often think that this perspective of beginning to understand our own seasons and organs holds such massive keys to the way we can choose to live our lives, to then make peace with the constant seeming conflict and paradoxes.

In her willingness to embrace graciously harrowing pain in her own body she was able to be the conduit to lift and transform others. She lived with a heavenly acceptance of what was beyond my understanding and served others despite, and because of, her own experience with pain; she lived having transcended it. There was no fixing or white washing the pain or running away from it; it was what it was and it, too, had its purpose.

So, the word, "connection" the seeking of connection or being cut off, for instance, are part of the facility that the lungs and large intestine give us. As we breathe in and let go in the cycles of life, we can connect ever deeper into a more wakeful conscious state. Nature does always show us the way.

Our lungs and large intestine collect and hold what is called our metal energy.

In Chinese Medicine the lungs and large intestine are paired up. We breathe in the air, our connection to life itself, and also will be simultaneously beginning to have a reaction from our large intestine. As we breathe in we are also letting go.

Can you imagine beginning to really understand that life requires us to take in, to breathe in and to let go? Without this concept in our cultural understanding, no wonder we are so cluttered up and no wonder we are collectively suffering from "stinking thinking." We are so often fermenting breweries, only responding to the stagnation of our large intestine.

Many patients have come to the clinics I had over the years with all sorts of large intestinal tract issues, as well as every possible sign and symptom, associated with the large intestine being out of balance. Symptoms such as abdominal pains, a sense of fullness, diarrhoea, mucus and blood in stools, thirst with no desire to drink, burning in anus, sparse dark urine, sense of heavy limbs and body, sweating that does not alleviate the fever, offensive smelling stools, were not uncommon.

A woman arrived in the clinic who was an international diamond dealer. Whilst she was brilliant in her field, and at work managed to look tidy, if you saw her outside of her work you would have been shocked. She appeared unkempt and messy, as if she no longer had any personal self-respect, wearing a film of sweat that was carefully masked during work by make-up.

She had almost lost all her eyelashes as she rarely took the make-up off properly, if at all. All her friends dressed exquisitely or had careers in the art world or high-end interior design. She was always seeking out the quality of her energetic imbalance. Whilst her intestinal tract actually was not holding on to anything she was losing all nutritional benefit. We do not associate loose stools, or long-term large intestinal issues, on a physical level, with loss of our self-respect or changes in hygiene standards. Nor do we consider that someone is actually attempting to replace the quality of what we call the metal energy. In this case, she was replacing the loss of her own metal energy with her particular choice of work, or friends. Both of which were providing some sustenance to that energy within her. After treatment and making some lifestyle changes her personal hygiene altered and it was obvious that her self-respect was improving hugely. She ended up with a varied group of friends, as she did not unconsciously need to replace the metal in her system. Initially she would arrive with cashmere, cotton and silks that had all seen better days. Once she had been treated for three months she turned up looking comfortable in new and clean clothes, but of the same quality materials.

One patient came to me complaining of breathing, digestion and sleeping issues with a racing pulse and feelings of anxiety. I knew that she had already seen numerous practitioners and had been bombarded by an assault course of tests in Western Medicine.

She had also tried a series of alternative therapies. By the end of the thorough and lengthy consultation, I told her that I thought I understood what her main root cause was and wanted to make a suggestion. With Traditional Chinese Medicine we are always looking for the roots of signs and symptoms.

First, I respectfully apologised that she had had such a horrible time. I had begun by apologising because, whilst I was not responsible, it was important to connect to the collective and unpleasant time she had had. Her constantly feeling a lack of any quality inside her made it vital that I acknowledge the very frightening, traumatic, and exhausting time that she had had. No one had given her any comfort or explanation of her very real symptoms.

It was imperative that I valued her real experience with no need to make all the previous practitioners wrong; which would not have supported her. I knew that I was just about to make a very simple but particularly unglamorous suggestion for which I deliberately was not going to get paid until and if it worked. This patient was very weepy in her voice; with an underlying catch in it as if so many unwept tears had got stuck. She was very exacting and in many respects cut off from her own inner qualities and outwardly not able to take in what we call the heavenly energy.

This woman was also wearing masses of bracelets all stacked on both wrists, big chunky metal fashion jewellery, very heavy make up over parched looking skin and was slightly dishevelled.

She softened, actually took a deeper breath and told me to go ahead and tell her what I thought.

"I do not give an immediate answer to what I think is happening. Usually, I like to go home taking time over all that you have told me working out a treatment plan before you return. In this case, I would like to suggest you do this: please, would you leave this office having not paid for this session, to then return in three weeks. In the interim, would you drink plain, room temperature water, sipping from a glass that I want you to have wherever you are? Over three to five days increase gently the two glasses to three, five and then six. Finally, over the last week see if you are able to drink just over a litre and a half of plain water through a day. Your last big drink of the day needs to be around 7 pm.

"You may experience your smell to change, your sense of heat to increase for a while, your urine to be far more and your bowels will begin to work after approximately the first three days. You also may experience some sensations of aches and pains, especially in your joints, a headache and even a hangover feeling. If you have any concerns, please call me".

"When you return in three weeks we will assess what has altered. Are you willing to try this for me, please?"

She nodded, a little dumbfounded.

"Any questions? Please keep a diary of all that you start experiencing. Bottled or filtered water would be better if your budget allows."

I knew that she did not live with a budget so every word out of my mouth was already part of treating her. Everything was about connecting her to her own body, precious needs, and her metal, Autumn season.

She had never been given any attention before medically that was so uniquely catering to her own individual life force and the disease that she was struggling with.

Three weeks later a totally different woman appeared in reception - lighter make-up, less bracelets, no chunky jewellery and an air of stillness about her.

With a broad and relaxed smile she said, "I have never ever felt better. By keeping my diary, which I actually have really enjoyed, I have working bowels, I am sleeping, have no racing heart, and my breathing has settled. The first two weeks were rather uncomfortable as you had told me, but as you had said that it would happen I began to trust you more."

This particular patient had never consistently drunk just plain water. Something so simple literally was at the root of her main issue, which was her constipation. The consequences of no water were beginning to be dire on every single level. Everything about her was telling me what was happening to her organs and therefore her essence. The cutting edge to her and anxiety had almost completely disappeared. In this instance an unglamorous suggestion, e.g. drinking water, had radically altered her health.

This is another example of a metal imbalance in the large intestine.

A very smart, immaculately dressed man walked into my office one day, barely waiting for the receptionist on duty to let me know he had arrived. It was not difficult to assess in a nanosecond that he was driven, overworked and an overachiever in all areas of his life. He sharply assessed if my treatment room was clean enough for him to sit down and if I myself indeed was someone to spend his precious time with. He was unyielding whilst totally commanding. Mostly bored with his life, he was used to being intimidating without fully being aware that the very thing he longed for, he himself pushed away. Feeling inadequate and empty, he sought a sense of wealth and richness outside of himself. It was very lucky that I had been brought up being around many similar characters so he was very familiar to me and I wasn't intimidated, but I was tired.

It had been a long day already. It was 7:00pm. I had just discovered that I was walking around with broken metal in my spine which made sense of what I had known was not right in me. The metal plates and bolts keeping me upright literally had one broken screw. At certain times in the day or night I had no strength left in my own structure. It had been too late to cancel him. He was a new patient so I had a long two hours or more ahead of me.

I asked him if he would like to have a tea with me, as I certainly was going to have one. I deliberately was putting out connection to him. He nonchalantly said yes he would.

Gathering myself for long enough for the kettle to boil and carefully laying a tray, I reminded myself that I was able to be beside this man whilst he unravelled what was eating away at him.

My new patient's energy was longing for quality, which he could not find within himself. I was connecting immediately to that for him. I knew that he would appreciate the glass, and the properly laid tray.

"I do not believe you can help me, but as you have come highly recommended I thought I would at least come and meet you."

The "highly recommended" had appealed to his internal disconnection to his own quality and was yet another clue to the state of this man's energy.

That was the beginning of what ended up being a very enjoyable two and half hours. As I understood the energy of the organs and where he was so stuck and struggling, it was easier for me to stick to the principles of my job at hand and not get caught into the personality traits that could so easily have made it a tricky time. I felt huge compassion for the cut off state he was in.

After I had finished, I again did the very unusual. These two stories are the only time I chose this particular tactic to immediately start treatment on someone, even though to them it would not initially have been considered a treatment.

"Thank you for answering all of those questions for me. I will consider taking you on as a patient on the following conditions."

I waited to see that one sentence sink in. Never will he have been talked to in that particular way. It had not occurred to him that I might not treat him.

He looked slightly uncertain and taken aback.

Laughing suddenly, he said to me, "Well, of all the things you could have said to me I would never have for a million years expected that! I am listening. What are your conditions?" With mischief in his voice, he actually delighted in the deliberate recognition and connection that I had created.

"I want you to leave here with a commitment to do a homework for yourself."

"Homework?!" he roared, almost losing the twinkle. "Damn, I haven't been given homework since I was 17. Are you serious?"

Nodding in as commanding way as possible, I continued connecting directly to him by looking straight at him.

"Each week for the next three weeks, I want you to find three people to whom you can make a significant difference financially. By the way, lump sums rarely work as they are not getting involved enough with the root causes of the financial lack. So you are going to have to use all of your genius to make a real and lasting difference to 9 separate individuals".

His eyebrows shot up, the bewilderment becoming shock across his face and giving me his alerted and at this point total concentration. I continued, "Without any of the nine knowing what you are up to, you have to do it anonymously. You need to find ways of respectively discovering who is right under your nose and struggling financially on a daily basis. As yet you have never even imagined these struggles are possible. In fact, you are so wealthy in terms of finances that you are now starving for connections and internal wealth in your own barren wasteland."

I let the shock sink in a little, as he was stunned into a complete silence. Already, immediately, though I could see he was engaged with the total novelty of the idea.

"I do not want you paying me for this treatment until you have returned. You do not value money – it is too easy for you to make it, so you will not value this prescription unless I value you enough to not get paid initially, or at all."

I stared at him with a deliberate kindness and softness that I felt whilst he searched my face for something familiar. It was imperative that I did not give it to him. He was almost too shocked to respond.

A bit later, he asked, "You are absolutely serious on both counts?"

"Yes."

"I am not supposed to understand, am I?"

"No."

"Okay."

The man in the immaculate suit shook my hand swiftly and left.

Certainly he had not for one moment expected me to respond to his deep-seated soul-sickness and depression with the instructions that I had left him with.

I had a six-week waiting list for new patients so it was imperative that I keep a slot available to him for when he was likely to come back. His secretary would ring more, so I arranged with the practise manager to leave an appointment free for the beginning of the fourth week. This attention to detail was necessary to ensure that he would not be disappointed when he would want to come in and tell me the outcome of his homework.

Life is so often being presented as if you can master it quickly, or in such a way as to not have any "shit" happening, or that you can "get your shit together" once and then that it will stay that way.

How great it would be if you actually began to appreciate the process that your own bowel is going through all of the time? That the movements you are having literally are transforming and helping you let go of your rubbish? That then you begin to see how much more quality of life you can bring to your days by gradually becoming aware of what you are asking your bowel to cope with?

It says a lot that we are having waste products floating in our seas that are larger than the UK and that is then, in part, a contributing factor to our waters being toxic to the wild life.

If we look at what we are putting into our bodies and begin to take more care over our own waste, we will be amazed at how our own health can be radically altered. Equally, we would think twice about tossing our litter into the streets or countryside.

Bowel movements can be a traumatic issue for many people. It is not a coincidence that as a nation we are not good at dealing with grief or our sadness, both so connected to our metal/autumn season.

My father in my childhood used to be rung up by many people asking him to help them to write their letters of condolences if someone important had died. He helped so many people face death and sad events. We are a nation so clogged up by our inability to express our grief, and then in the paradox of life we do not master being joy fuelled in contrast.

The gifts and functions of our lungs and large intestine help us continually transform what we are inhaling and letting go of. Once we fully absorb the fact that we are going to be on a voyage of letting go all of the time, we can actually get on with embracing what we take in. We can begin to see that every single one of us is struggling with some kind of sadness and grief.

Life is presented as a series of endless, quick, outside fixes or as if we as humans have control, rather than being shown that we do indeed have the tools for self-mastery. Surely, though, one of the amazing honours of our lives is actually transforming our journeys into something that takes us home to ourselves. It is the rhythms of our lives, the literal body, mind and spirit promptings that can and do keep us going. To keep believing the illusions that are so powerfully pedalled is dangerous if you think in terms of what havoc constipation or loose stools cause.

When we are insidiously not realising our healthy need for qualitative connections on so many levels, we merely delay the mastering of ourselves. Because our systems are built to know and recognise vibrant energetic health, you can imagine how much energy it is taking to be becoming more and more dis-eased.

The capacity to unravel dis-ease at its roots is totally built into our systems, and functions no matter what. Then, without even thinking about it, we have a series of functions taking place that are unconsciously going on all of the time. We really do have the ability to respond, almost naturally and even unconsciously, to the events, people, places and things outside of us that we have no control over.

If we understood that our body masterfully protects us continually, that if we willingly guided it in directions that adhered more to the natural cycles of our lives then we would be having less resistance. The more resistance we have internally in our organs literally means that we automatically become magnets to the same on the outside of ourselves, and with far less capacity to deal with the externals.

So, the word "connection," for instance, is part of the facility that the lungs give us, which is discussed in the next chapter. As we breathe in and let go in the cycles of life, we can connect ever deeper into a more wakeful conscious state.

The "immaculate" suit returned exactly at the time that we had left a slot open for him.

With a beaming and totally transformed energy he bounded in to the treatment room. He was almost like a buoyant teenager, very excited. Unnervingly though he sat down, crossed his legs, became very quiet staring at me with clearly amazement written all over his face. I got the distinct impression that if he could he would have taken my head off and tried to examine it so I started to laugh.

"Are you normally so accurate with your hit seeking missiles?"

Side stepping answering, which he knew I would, I asked him

"SO how did you find three weeks of looking out for others, and anonymously?"

His cut off and exacting energy had dispersed, the pent up sadness had been replaced and turned into a open curiosity about life and everyone, now even the practitioner sitting in front of him, who he had not expected to be able to really help him. We both knew that he had only come out of an idle, but disengaged, curiosity in the first place and certainly not expecting any real help at all with what he had not exactly understood himself.

"I honestly had no idea what a difference I could make to others' lives. I adore the challenges of really bothering with everyone who are right under my own nose. Doing it anonymously is glorious. No one understands what on earth has come over me. Even my friends are getting reviewed rather differently. All the agitation, sense of listlessness and of even being bored has totally gone. It has actually blown my mind to see what money can do to the lives of those who are not used to being able to solve their problems. The issues in their lives are based on not having enough money, or opportunities. My whole team at work seems happier. I guess I have been a very tricky person to work for, as I have been so stuck up really, caught up in my own Ivory Tower. I thought that fable was only about women. I have all these means and yet they were backing up on me, weren't they?"

"It has made me determined to make more of what I am so good at, helping others. The clever part is not to be generally seen to doing any of it. So that I am not using a sort of charity, or patronising attitude. I would hate that myself so I am assuming that others would too. Perhaps others do not begrudge me so much what comes so easily to me but that I have been taking it all for granted or making good use of it to benefit others.

Summary of Large Intestine Chapter.

The large intestine is associated with the Autumn Season

The element is Metal

The colour is grey/white

The sound is weeping

The odour is rotten

The emotion/energy is grief and sadness

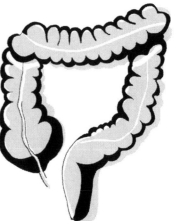

The function of this organ is to drain the rubbish that cannot be utilised

The associated organ is Lungs (chapter 2)

A balanced Autumn provides the ability:

- to take in the richness of life

- to feel and move on from losses, rather than getting stuck in a perpetual unresolved sense of loss

- to accept that when something is over, complete, then it is imperative that we let go

Behaviours that can become evident when the autumn/metal goes out of balance which we and others can sense in us are:-

Feeling/being nonchalant	to	being deeply moved
Feeling/being messy and polluted	to	craving quality and purity
Seeking connection	to	feeling cut off
Feeling overworked	to	feeling resigned/inert
Feelings of fragility	to	rigid / intransigent / dogged

Chapter 2

Discover your

Lungs

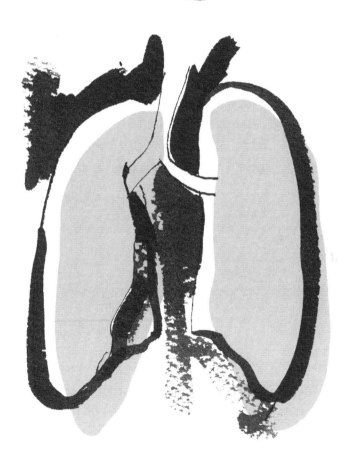

Inner knowledge is the key to your outer wealth, no matter what!

Discover your Lungs

The season for the lungs, part of your metal element, is Autumn.

Collecting Qi, energy from, what is described as, the heavenly realms.

Emotion: sadness and grieving

The sound is weeping, which an experienced practitioner will be able to detect in the tones of your voice if your lungs or large Intestine, your metal element is out of balance.

The emotion is grief so if and when you are in balance, within your own energy, you will be able to grieve appropriately. In other words to allow your mind, body and Spirit to continue the process of living whilst also grieving your loss, losses and responding to sad events in ways that keep your own energy moving.

A lack of grief, being cut off, disconnected, feeling or acting as if you are inadequate or uninspired, seeking completion and approval from outside of yourself are all indications that your metal is out of balance.

We have an incredibly restricted idea of grief in the West. The Grief Recovery® institute teaches about the normal response to life's continuous events is to be living in the midst of conflicting emotions. For example because Grief is not confined to just the narrow events of death or the dying, on our dream wedding day we can be thrilled and happier than we ever thought possible, whilst also sad that our life with our flatmates is over and we just know that inevitably our future will be different.

Society allows the so-called 'positive' emotions, but has this constant banter around what is perceived as the 'negative'. Certainly not allowing for the honest, normal human experience of actually two or more emotions happening at the same time. So from a early stage in life we are taught to start hiding at least half of what is actually happening routinely to us all. No wonder the more the marketing world gets insidiously into every area of our lives do we begin to think our image is the vital thing that we need to concentrate on.

Living your life as if image is the most important thing is leading to a very empty internal level of increasing bankruptcy. A group of children chose half an hour of being a celebrity in exchange for their education when a random survey was done recently.

As a personal example I was so crushed inside myself, initially, by my younger and very bizarre life that I really believed that I was polluted in some ways. So my outward image was something of huge trauma to me as I seriously believed that I was hideous. I tried to hide in all sorts of differing ways, almost in an attempt to protect others from what I was so convinced about. The polluted behaviour that had been imposed upon me earlier, along with the genetic disorder that I was carrying from certainly three generations, all had left me with a very distorted sense about myself. I was certainly cut off from any sense of my value. I constantly thought I was going to be judged. There was truth to my misery as I was being judged, humiliated and bullied at home so it did not take much for me to project that on to the world. Assuming that I was to be bullied externally, I desperately tried to do whatever it would take to fit in with how I perceived the world to be. My image was bound up in a very sad need to be approved of, as I was not experiencing much at home.

Although my father gave me an incredible sense of my value on the one hand, connecting all the time with me, other factors in the family dynamics were far louder.

I was constantly having chest, and excruciating ear infections after the first surgery that had been done to me when I was seven. I was almost entirely deaf for the first seven years of my life so the huge shock and trauma of sound, after that first surgery, also impacted my life massively. Of course in those days it never occurred to anyone the impact that sound would have on me. I vividly remember thinking that everyone was shouting at each other. My parents, inevitable, separation was already on the cards so the tension in our home was like a relentless pitch that shattered like glass in me continuously. No wonder both my brother and I were actually relieved when they separated. I was pleased and unhappy all at once. That is the nature of our walk with the energy of our lungs. As we breathe in, we are letting go.

Some signs and symptoms of a lung imbalance are shortness of breath, weak voice, easily catching colds, tiredness, watery sputum, pale white complexion, spontaneous daytime sweating, Dry coughs or dry mouth and throat, weak and hoarse voice, A dislike of speaking, Body aches with runny nose, stuffiness in the chest, loose stools. Seemingly inappropriate grief, Malar flush, occipital headaches, poor appetite, Wheezing, feeling clogged up, heaviness, fuzziness or dizziness of the head.

From a very early age I was going from one symptom to another, mostly being told that my real problem was hypochondria, attention seeking or demanding and selfish thoughtlessness. Nothing though could have been further from the truth, but I did not know that for a very long time. If something is said often enough at a very early age there is no reason for you to necessarily not believe it to be true. Constantly being given very little understanding medically or from most of my family, was also a tough contributing factor to me feeling generally somehow messy and polluted in differing ways. My focus began to be getting my 'act' together. Dealing with whatever it was that made me clearly so 'unacceptable', or unworthy of real connection. The harder I tried the worse everything became, as I was not at all what I was being told or in fact the problem. The alcoholism in our family midst was hiding the very genetic matrix that I was struggling with. Two generations had used every type of mood altering behaviour or substance to self-medicate the pain and total malfunctioning going on in every single aspect of their bodies. The mental health of various family members, who had huge and terrifying impacts on my life, were a very small aspect of what medically was horribly wrong with each member.

I learnt from a very early age to hide any physical, let alone emotional pain that I experienced. My digestion was not working, gynaecologically I was already in trouble so had been put on the pill at the age of 11. Almost overnight a couple of years later the collagen in my body just lost its ability to operate. Tennis, riding, running, fencing, tap dancing, even Russian dancing which had been one of my party tricks, abruptly came to a dramatic halt as I was carted off to receive 11 weeks of traction in hospital. I had been finding such solace in movement so literally to collapse and be removed from my friends one day and put into hospital was a devastating shock. I never returned to school and was put to bed for a year of treatments. One of the memories I have of my time in the hospital was thinking I was going to die and then being rather disappointed that I did not. I had no way of understanding that I was grieving deeply all that I loved, so to me it was like a death. As well as deeply confusing to have something wrong that was not based on my, by this time, apparently, growing character flaws. Discussions about my utter failure as a human were endless whilst the ones about what actually was preventing me from having any control over my own body were nil. What I was taking in from my breathing onwards was not very palatable.

Slowly, and later on as a young woman there were aspects of my behaviour that did change as my self-respect and worth improved. I learnt to stop the bullying that I had been doing to myself, learnt from others, which then stopped the subtle invitation to the outside world.

So as you also become aware of what and why you are doing certain things you can strengthen your own metal. Literally in the way that you respond to another is displaying how energetically balanced your organs are. As we are not taught to really listen to each other we nearly all over lay each other's conversations with our own noise and needs. The connections that we so long for with each other are something that from the second we have a conversation with another, is missed entirely.

When we are in balance though we can feel loss and move on as the Autumn season within us literally sheds its leaves and moves on, making way for the new. We can take in the richness of life, whilst accepting that grief is an important aspect of our lives. Which in turn then means that we are far less 'noisy' in our own beings when with others. So we can pick up the endless cues to have meaningful connections, not being so cut off or aloof, even stuck up.

Over the years it became easier and more straightforward to key into others' lack of connection to the quality of living. This following story tells the story of a woman who had the Metal in balance when the time came for the most devastating loss of her life.

She was gardening when she saw the Vicar coming down the street of the tiny village she lived in. It was a time when the local Vicar brought important news. She knew by the way he walked, with his head bent deep in thought that he was coming with bad news.

She stopped what she was doing and waited at the gate for him, putting out her hand and warmly welcoming him. Every time he was about to talk she would interrupt him with a question.

"Would you like a Cup of tea?"

"Yes, thank you, but I have……………."

"I have homemade cake, would you like some cake?"

"That would be kind but I have …………

"You take a seat; I shall be back in a while with a tray. Enjoy the view."

Baffled, the vicar sat down as he realised that she was not going to let him speak.

At last she returned, pouring them both a cup of tea, cutting a slice of cake.

Turning to him once he had some of the tea and a few mouthfuls of the cake with great composure she said:

"You have come to tell me my husband is dead haven't you?"

"Yes I am afraid I have"

After they had discussed the details of her husband's death, the Vicar asked if he could ask her a question.

"When you knew what I had come for, why did you offer me tea and cake, looking after my needs at such a time? I personally married you and your husband. I knew how much you adored each other."

"Yes indeed we did. However when my mother brought me up she taught that whenever you have terrible news, that you immediately think you cannot handle, you must stick to your routines. It is your routines that will hold you and your days together when nothing else will. I never forgot that, so when I saw you coming down the village, I had had already a sense of George being dead, so I wanted to stay focused on what would I normally have been doing. In this case it was to have tea with you, welcoming you. I understand now what it is that I need to do. Later I will put the potatoes on and continue with the mundane. In that way I will honour the glorious majesty of what we were given for so long with each other. His time to go to our Lord was never going to be my timing. Thank you so much for giving me news that must have been so difficult for you. Yes, you are right I so loved that man. In his death I will continue to love him but he will want me to live, which although not easy I will."

Generally we are so collectively blocked in our Metal element that we simply do not know how to handle grieving or transforming change. Very sadly, suicides amongst men and young people are increasing with seeming no one really necessarily understanding why. Similarly, many people do not understand why many people are having tattoos at the moment. Or the increase in body piercing has massively increased without people necessarily knowing why they are motivated to put 'metal' parts into their bodies. Fashion and sexual gratification, depending on the positions of the body piercing, is not totally the whole motivation.

Many patients came to me with severe menstrual issues, often with a piece of jewellery pierced through their belly button. We call it the energetic hub of the entire body so sooner rather than later, when the patients are ready, I asked them to reconsider their choices. At the very least, once educated as to what literally a 'SPOKE' is doing to the very sophisticated systems, gives valuable information that is needed to make decisions wisely.

In Integrated Chinese Medicine there is no judgment, only constant assessments of how the balance of individual or collective energy is. From a diagnostic perspective, both the tattooing and the increase in suicides, self-harming and self-destructive behaviours is due, in part, to the lack of connection to living with quality and connection. How we are in thought, word and deed is so influenced by what we are literally connecting ourselves to, what our Lungs and Large Intestine is taking in and then letting go of.

We are not taught how to handle, or even to know that life is full of contrast, contradictions and conflicting emotions. Collectively we side-line, ignore or blank the real contexts that change is bringing about. We stuff our energetic and emotional responses particularly, whilst we are not actually learning the point of our own bodies in an integrated way. We are not being universally taught, yet, how interconnected every single aspect of living, breathing, eating and behaving is. The emphasis in our education is relatively narrow for how much is going on all of the time in our bodies, minds and spirits.

I am so aware as I sit at my spanking new computer that I am only interested right now in writing this book, so I rather impatiently want to continue. So when a message asks me if I want a tour of this new computer the answer is emphatically no, not yet. A big mistake no doubt, as I stubbornly make the job in hand so much more difficult.

That is exactly like so much of our lives.

The computer is so full of information, capabilities and potential to support and actually help me do this project, yet I will, if I am honest, probably never ever tap even two percent of its potential. So that is a very good analogy for our own bodies. We literally are so full of incredible capacities for dealing with the realities of our lives. Living though as if each aspect of us is separate and that there are not constant feedback mechanisms going on is a risky way to get the most out of our lives.

When speaking to many parents at present, young people are so bombarded with misinformation about life, and being fed literally rubbish that they are collectively suffering from low self-esteem, low-grade depressions, if not full-blown depressions. The time has not arrived yet when medical practitioners combine all the incredible and amazing solutions that there are already out there for dynamic health to flourish. We are not yet collectively at a level that we are only solution orientated. In the English culture, we are still problem orientated.

Younger adults are being sold all sorts of things for instance to put on their skin, under their arms, even creams and scents for between their legs. As younger people can be quite literal, what sort of message is this giving them about their own bodies? We describe the skin as being your third lung, so from that context why would you want to put so many products on your skin, which are being absorbed into your body.

One of the most shocking, overwhelming aspects of being diagnosed with a serious illness is that you can be propelled head first into an entirely new world of discovering what you have been doing so blindly and unconsciously to poison your own body. Suddenly you may well be thrown by having to radically alter all the products you use, from your shampoos, soaps, shower products to all of your household products, as well as make up, shaving products. Your dishwasher and washing machine powders may seriously be a disrupting factor to your integrated health.

A balanced metal element will be able to let go of what does not work, clearing away rubbish on all levels, whilst replacing what has gone with the next levels of development. There is a housing project in the world that is recycling all of the waste product from the humans living in the buildings. It will never be a coincidence that as we ourselves are cleaned from the inside out, with differing choices, that we begin to notice how much is being done around the world to deal with our waste products in more sustainable ways.

One of my themes during my work was, and still is, that dynamic energetic health is possible in the midst literally of dying. It is possible in the midst of appalling circumstances on many, many differing circumstances to continue to find your deep inner sense of vitality that actually can override any prognosis or appalling of circumstances.

Unravel dis-ease naturally is a way of seeing, feeling and experiencing our lives in ways that are continually liberating. Which then in turn gives us the inspiration to live dynamically through our realities, even transforming and connecting to what our own solutions, to our issues and challenges are.

As in iridology, reflexology and tongue diagnosis, as examples, inner knowledge becomes the key to outer wealth.

In the Grief Recovery process, that I was initially involved in bringing to the UK, they teach how to actually recover, not forget, from all sorts of losses. It is so incredibly sad when you hear so many people talk about "never ever being able to recover" from a loss, as by really believing that, they are sealing their fate to illness further on down the road, unknowingly.

Very early on in my practise, I had the privilege of meeting an extraordinary woman. By the skin of my very early and inexperienced teeth, I managed to be able to look beyond her outer appearance and see her "brilliance and inner wealth". I had been called to do a home visit, which had given me an even deeper and instant knowledge into her world. The smell as she opened her door hit me, frankly having me almost gagging. It was a rotting stench with clearly cats living in almost every spot that was not cluttered. Everywhere I looked was messy and stank of rotting waste. Her own body mass fell off her in huge folds as if somehow disconnected to her own precious body that she was clearly cut off from. She had piles and piles of things that she was working on, seemingly all at once. She was so ill, hardly able to breathe or move around and yet, when I looked at the quality of her work, it was exquisite. She worked on the most precious of silk rugs with the occasional dress design for a wealthy Indian Princess. The Princess would send her butler around to collect the dresses. Again, they were of the finest material and could not have been more exquisitely and perfectly made.

When I asked this woman a host of questions, it was easy to see how disconnected she was from her own talents, her own inner and very refined wealth. It was as if she had had so much grief that she was almost dying, with too many leaves having died on top of her. She had got stuck in an everlasting Autumn energy that was now totally out of balance.

The worse her sense of inner poverty, disconnection and grief became, the more trapped she was in literally her own (with the cat's litter boxes) rotting skin. Her skin had so many folds of blubber that she had sores, some of which were infected. She refused to see a Doctor or nurse.

Starting treatment immediately I was able to do something that basically gives the entire body a chance to breathe again and get rid of what it has become overwhelmed by. I then rooted her treatment and asked her who else had a key to her home. A dear friend had a set and was popping in regularly. I arranged to return the next day telling her that she would probably sleep for at least ten to twelve hours.

I treated her intensively for 6 weeks, two, sometimes three times weekly in her home, until she was well enough to come to the clinic. The clinical and integrated intention was to let her own body find its way with her stacked and stuck rotting autumns, to invite her own body to find its own inner wealth again so that she connected to, and began to take care of herself.

Within six weeks she had lost about two stone, her skin had begun healing, a shine had come back into her eyes, with her hair, that had hung in a limp dirty fashion to her face, beginning to get some life back into it. She had even begun to tidy up the mess she lived in.

She had begun to talk about all the losses in her life. I was able to witness the intense realities of them, showing her how important and vital it was for her to be allowed to grieve. To let go when crying was her body's way of releasing more of her deep losses. Her whole life had been a non-stop series of dreadful losses. It was so astounding to me that she was able to function at all. It was easy to show her the deep respect that I felt. She was highly acclaimed in certain worlds but when I asked her about her fame, the weeping noise and tone would become more pronounced and she would become more distressed and then cut off. I was very careful to be an example of what she had forgotten long, long ago, to be connecting her to what we call the heavenly realms.

I gradually started setting her homework that gave her connection - a sense of being complete and meaning again. The death of her brother when she was thirteen, whom she had adored and did everything for, as he was disabled from birth, had had a profound effect on her as she began realising that also she lost her parents with his death as they did not know how to recover at all from his death. To work one evening a week as a volunteer with disabled children teaching them quilting was hugely healing to her. She quite suddenly and literally started arriving at the clinic as the relatively young and still very much attractive woman that she was. She was also suddenly commissioned to work on a very famous tapestry in France which would mean trips to a glorious Chateau. She was able to take in the literal wealth of her own talents. Within 9 months she was totally unrecognisable.

I normally did not cross over the boundaries of patient - practitioner relationship but when I received a gold embossed Christmas invitation to her home I accepted, as I really wanted to take the opportunity to see how well she was doing, in her own home now after such huge changes. She was clearly coming out of her years in isolation.

In Integrated Chinese Medicine we are trained to be seeing, hearing and assessing every single detail of another person's life. It is a sacred privilege that I was taught to take as one of the greatest honours that would ever become before me. The more details we know to take, in very specific areas, the simpler a diagnosis can become.

Each organ, once you begin the journey of connecting to it's functioning on all levels that is working for and on behalf of you, the simpler it is to master what I call your own inner wealth.

In the twelve step fellowships that are growing around the world, it is suggested that the more you focus on yourself in healthy ways and the less you focus on others in unhealthy ways, the easier and more peaceful your own life becomes. However, by unravelling our own illusions of ourselves and beginning to treat ourselves with more self respect, for instance, we in turn can than be more respectful to others. It is also suggested that to become healthier, happier and more peaceful, it is absolutely vital that we serve one another. By serving others, we serve ourselves.

By responding to others, though, through the lens of our own misconceptions about ourselves, we can enable more of the problems rather than the solutions. Hence it becomes paramount that the focus always has to be taking responsibility for our own inner wealth first, to be of real value to others in our world.

Your own self-mastery becomes the greatest way to build your own skills and purpose. Your own connections to your own precious life can then be meaningful. The idea is, that the more you are connected to your own truth and the more you have made it a priority to know yourself, the more present and available you are to others, as well as the world. You start living connected to your world, rather than disconnected, isolated and cut off from the endless consequences of your actions.

However, when you are a practitioner trained in the ways that I was, you get to be in the position to make prescriptions for others according to their energetic inner accounts. The focus and intention is always to connect clients and patients to their own bodies, spirits and minds in an integrated way. I always used to feel as if I was an energetic accountant.

In fact one of my favourite teachers who taught me, with other fantastic and inspiring teachers, used to say that it was our job in part to break the credit card mentality that our culture now takes as the norm. He taught that from his perspective, part of the reasons why there was increasing illness and inflammatory conditions, was simply because everyone was being encouraged to live way beyond their means.

Increasingly society is hooked into an instant gratification attitude, with, at the same time, a credit card mentality, as he called it, endlessly overstretched financially and emotionally. An example, routinely now, is the consultants I am under, both private and NHS who have secretaries or administrators who can be looking after up to seven consultants. Every single time I talk to these incredible people, I can hear in their voices how totally overstretched they are. With the credit mentality i.e. "we have collectively bought the idea that it is OK to live continually overstretched". However, the more we overstretch ourselves, the more that we will be at the mercy of continual reaching out for instant gratification. Thereby we begin to live in a vicious circle which is the very opposite of inner wealth.

So as practitioners if we were not willing to really engage with the belief systems setting up the dynamics of illness, then this same teacher did not believe we would make great practitioners. To radically alter perceptions of energy, money and others' own life force, it had to be a daily part of our own lives, to challenge ourselves. He really alerted us to how counterproductive our own and patients beliefs were going to be to our work. Finding solutions to issues and energetic problems was not our real issue. The real difficulty would be supporting people to value the solutions that were possible, as we are a society so hooked into drama, problems and being victims of apparently what we have no control of.

Sometimes the Metal imbalance can be like having a giant disposal unit where no matter what delicious, lovingly prepared food and sustenance is prepared for you, the whole lot goes down, almost unseen, unappreciated, certainly not connected to and is then trashed. When we are disconnected from our own inner wealth, meeting a friend in a restaurant can result in a performance/drama. As the table sitting, placement of the chairs, where the door is placed, anything and everything will be a constant reason to not quite settle or connect with what is in front of you.

A metal out of balance can be a glass half full mentality or almost mid-sentence when you are operating from real inner poverty you can cut straight through people, almost as if a knife has descended.

So back to the patient and her happy ending party, the evening arrived. As I walked in I was met by a lovely smiling waiter in crisp black and white uniform, to a house that was totally unrecognisable. It was smart, tidy, flowers were everywhere, the clutter had gone and everything was in its place. There seemed to be only one rather regal looking cat wandering around the radiant, now slim patient was standing in her own drawing room holding court, her head tipped back with a glorious sound of rich laughter. She was radiating her own inner wealth.

When our lungs are functioning at an optimum energetic level, you will be able to take in the richness of life, literally.

A client came to see me for some grief recovery work. He was very self-aware and knew that he could not go into his future successfully in his present state of "stuck ness"

"My wife would not want me to be living half-heartedly whilst waiting until I see her again "

"I have been widowed relatively young, however when I promised her that I wouldn't let my grief take over, I hadn't anticipated what the actual reality of her dying would do to me. I know that it has triggered a situation from my young teens that I have never ever been able to tell anyone".

So we carefully laid the foundation for him to energetically be able to move beyond the pain cycles that he was in. They were not going to stop until his body, spirit and mind had spat out, almost literally at times what needed to be witnessed, acknowledged and healed.

The time came which was very momentous for him to read out a letter that was releasing the emotional charge in the pain. He had begun almost twisted in a physical ball of tight wretchedness, which as he read loosened, tears poured from his face, his body shook, his colouring kept changing in nanoseconds in front of me. I sat silently allowing him to carry on at his own pace. He finished, sighed and went slightly limp as the briefest of smiles appeared on his face. I said nothing allowing the silence to descend like the glorious first coating of thick snow. No more than about six minutes into a palpable comfortable silence we both heard a loud grunting below the treatment room.

"Is that what I think it is?"

"Yup, I think it really is. A new tenant has just this week moved in "

Clearly a woman in the throes of total bliss and passion was beginning to shout loudly with a frenzy of pleasure as an all embracing orgasm was flooding her body.

The patient and I looked at each other and roared with laughter.

"My wife would have loved that timing!"

"I already feel totally different. Life is beckoning me, perhaps though I am not quite up for doing that with another woman..........yet "

With a very mischievous glint in his eye he left, our work clearly complete.

A shift in the season within him had returned him to remembering his wife with pleasure and joy, but no longer wincing in an agony that was not only due to her loss. Would it mean that he wouldn't feel sad again.

Absolutely not!

It is always and in all ways about finding your own individual balance with all the events that will keep happening. He had already accessed a huge amount of his own inner and outer wealth so it was far easier for him to recognise when he was stuck. He was not confused about what that meant. He was used to calling in experts of different fields, constantly willing to improve on his knowledge of himself and the world. He already believed and lived by the knowledge that his outer wealth was only a real manifestation of his inner wealth, as he had wondrously explained to me on our first meeting.

"You see, even in my wife's absence, I want and need to honour our incredible life together by continuing to be my best now. We have two glorious children. Who, although young adults need me to keep being present to their needs and lives ahead of them. I know enough about grief and not properly grieving that I will not be able to be fully present to them or my days if I do not allow myself to recover. It does not mean that I will ever forget my soul mate, but life is still here for me to live fully. My wife believed that it was possible to have more than one soul mate and used to tease me that I was just being controlling with the taps of abundance"

I remember asking him about what he thought she had meant.

With a fantastic twinkle that always came up when he talked about his wife he told me

"Abundance is all around us, there is such an endless supply but we have control of the taps so mostly we live on trickles of abundance. So it's typical, my wife told me that I would assume that there could only be one woman for me. Or, when she really wanted to tease me, one man for her. She was very grounded and also now I sense that she knew that she wouldn't make old bones so I think she was always preparing me for her death. I loved that she challenged my thinking and beliefs, always making me turn on the taps more inside!"

Simple (But Not Necessarily Easy) Tips for Vibrant Inner Wealth, and Tantalising Teasers

Every single aspect of your life is about energy, either the movement and flow of it or the stagnation of it with its consequences.

Most people want, or need, approval and connections and yet we live in a world now that does not do connections, despite all the machines that are apparently making it easier. Do not seek out more superficial connections as it will increase the sense of worthlessness with also a low grade sense of depression. Several articles about, what a dear friend calls Face ache, Facebook, have written about how miserable and dis-connected people can feel spending time on social media. It is sometimes like being on the outside of a party that is constantly just unreachable to you. When and if you are already suffering with loneliness to be scrolling through others highlights which does not honestly reflect a life can become distressing. So clarify your intention with using social media so that you are in charge of it, rather than insidiously it is in charge of you.

So, declutter, cleanse and sort out what is worn out, not working and continues to muddle your steps forward and through your days.

Make up your mind how many shirts for instance do you really use, need or want. Start having the notion that everything in your life needs a constant flow of energy, fresh air. So when you are buying something new, deliberately let go of something old. The more conscious you are of what you are doing, the more quality you will notice you start having in your life.

When you buy something, ask yourself, is it a 10/10 e.g. does it really make you feel great, or do you really need it. If the answer is "Yes", and it does not overstretch you, then allow yourself to have it. Or be honest with yourself, are you using it for instant gratification?

Bother about the details of your life.

Is your car spanking new and clean, but your cupboard with your clothes in, a tip?

Are you careless with your clothes, are your shoes scuffed or wrecked?

Every single aspect of how you present yourself every single day is a loud statement of the state of the organs.

Interesting that so many men are now having their bottoms, literally hanging out of their trousers. With no awareness of what it means in prison situations, they blindly follow fashion whilst potentially messing up their hip actions. If they wanted to become great lovers and if there was proper respectful access to teaching men how to be great lovers, these young men would change in a heartbeat. Young men are not given even remotely, enough support to know what or how to master their sexuality, masculinity let alone their dress.

It is said that the elder women of one tribe show the younger men how to be lovers, and that is why there is no domestic violence at all amongst them.

So if you are a man, find some other men who you admire, who live with an integrated view of life. Be open to learning and embracing new ideas. `Connect to what you are doing, eating, wearing and thinking'. There is a chapter later about sexuality.

Boxer shorts are known to be much more cooling for men - making a difference to sperm count. Whereas Y fronts keep the scrotums temperature raised. Become aware of overheating between your legs. For both men and women what, how and where we are wearing underwear impacts hugely on the health of our energy.

If you really want to master your incredible body, build on its never ending potential. Research Tai Chi, Qi Gong or any Martial Arts. Have the willingness to connect to your own courage and find out how to add real quality to your individual life. Who do you admire and why? .

Whilst similarly, women are not being given opportunities to grow into self-respect, with a recognition of their deep and individual value. Are your nails chipped, do you go to work or about your day not even noticing, or even having a care, for how your fingers and hands look Your hands and your face are a huge reflection of what you think of yourself.

How much are you connecting your make up rituals with self-respect, approving and loving, cherishing yourself or is it a way of hiding from the world with a mask that you think you have to have?

Some of my patients would ask me where was I was going, as I always dressed smartly. They were surprised by my answer.

"I am dressing out of respect for you, it would be awful for you to have to come to me if I looked a wreck". "My father taught me to be respectful of others and always make the most of myself as a sign of respect for whoever I was with."

When he knew I was coming home he would always put on a fresh shirt and tie. It was a very important sign to me of his conscious awareness of loving me with his own self-respect. As he suffered from blinding headaches, pain and a massive disability, it would have been so easy for him to constantly be presenting me with how he must have so often felt. He never did, in that he always bothered with himself and therefore me. He did share his reality emotionally but never with any self-pity.

So ask yourself what you are doing with how you wear your mental state, as well as how you present yourself. Are you drawing attention to the mess you feel by being a mess. Experiment with how much better you feel in your days if you bother with how you dress. Your emotional and varying states do not have to be in charge of you. You are in charge increasingly of your own amazing being.

The colours you wear will make a difference to your mood.

Have you the spare cash to have some help with what colours and style actually suit you and literally will pop your character and natural colourings? IF you have the money, then ask for help from a professional. IF you cannot afford professional help, then put yourself in a mirror and drape, one at a time, a colour over your shoulders and front. If you are a woman do it without makeup. If you are a man ask a woman to do it with you as this exercise will literally make shopping, which most men hate for themselves, let alone their spouses, even quicker and easier. Your face and sense of yourself will literally deflate with the wrong colours. Or you will feel

'POPPED' in your energy. Have fun with this one day.

Bother to connect with what and how you like to live. What is it that lifts your spirit, who and what inspires you? Allow yourself to complete jobs around your home, to complete with things you say you are going to do. Monitor when you leave things incomplete. Become someone that you like to live with. What character traits do you like in others, start practising them. If you know that you are a person who sees the glass as half empty start 'FAKING TO MAKE IT', in other words practise seeing the glass as half full.

Every single night before you go to sleep literally make a list of all that you are grateful for 5 new things each and every day.

Complete your day with gratitude, no matter what.

Also add at night a conscious decision to recognise and approve of 5 things that you have done in your day. Think through 5 things in a day that have inspired you that you accomplished. Build on your own internal wealth account, inner knowledge of yourself. Review honestly what could have been done differently, better or with less stress. Be willing to continually keep your side of the street clean, e.g. you cannot change others behaviour but it is you that you will constantly live with. So become someone you like who is not afraid to admit they are wrong and say so.

Whatever size you are and whatever your own relationship with yourself is, are you willing to become best friends with yourself?

What would self-respect and self-loving acceptance and approval look like? How can you connect to your unique qualities?

Think through much more consciously what you are putting on your skin and why. Vitamin D levels are dropping as we all now put far too much sun blocks and screens and so our bodies do not get access to the Vitamin D levels that need to be topped up. Just because an advert says you need something get into the habit of educating yourself and finding out the truth.

Notice that as you breathe, continuously and ideally deeply, increasingly consciously you are also literally having your intestinal tract creating mulch that you will be letting go of daily. You have an average of five feet of large intestines, so with the lungs, and your skin collecting and holding, what exactly are you consciously collecting and holding?

Without any judgment, ask yourselves these questions and jot down the answers.

Are you really seeking approval in the wrong places, wrong events and wrong friendships for your particular real personality?

What are you doing to feel complete?

What do you need to start connecting to your own inner qualities of "OKness", to the inner purity where you stop picking at yourself?

How are you connecting, finding inspiration and meaning in your life?

What energises you and helps you to connect to the heavenly realms?

What do your heavenly realms even mean to you?

When you listen to stunning music, are you transported somewhere that you need and want repeated?

Are you willing to look at your accounts financially to see if you can rearrange how and what you are spending your money on.

Are you willing to go through the grief involved in, initially sorting out your financial accounts, in order to achieve some more quality in your life? Ann Wilson has made her life about educating people to financial freedom. Find ways of allowing yourself that education around your own finances.

Layer by layer, season by season, change is predictably happening, which when we are willing to learn to go with, we can have ever increasing richness of life. That does not mean however that we necessarily get what we want, when we want it.

Your essence, spirit and soul have an agenda that does get fulfilled sooner or later. If you begin to connect with that, you can therefore master your journey in an integrated way.

Where are you refusing to have movement in your life, taking in and letting out or letting go?

Grief and sadness is a necessary and continual part of life. From the perspective of integrated living it is vital that you allow yourself to learn the skills necessary in grieving. So that what is a natural process does not become something that ends up throttling your energy, then your life. Unexpressed and incomplete emotional connections to those you have loved, and lost can stop you from fully living or even loving again.

Turn to those who have been also stuck in devastating loss, who know how to literally walk you through the tools you need to recover, replacing the misinformation with helpful, life enhancing tools.

Look up Carol Henderson - the Grief Recovery Method®, in the UK or

A survey was recently done of school children. They wanted 30 minutes of being famous, over and above their education.

That is really an energetic statement of how imbalanced the metal is now in our society. Our children are seeking approval, recognition with a sense of adequacy in the rare moments when a celebrated person will be in the limelight. They have no sense of the prices the people pay for fame, the hard work and often terrible isolation that goes with the life of a famous person. The children are associating the glitter, applaud, seeming momentary attention as something that would fill the gap within them. It does not! It takes a very centred, wise, and knowing person to handle fame well and without believing that somehow you are so elevated that you can get away with behaving incredibly badly to others.

The lungs can connect us to the heavenly realm and inner wealth within and therefore is the key to outer wealth. What does your heavenly realm and inner wealth look like to you?

In the next Chapter, I introduce you to some aspects of your kidneys and the bills that we unintentionally end up paying for. Events, bills or even relationships that, unresolved, end up affecting our lives.

Summary of the Lungs Chapter

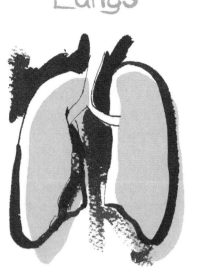

Lungs

The Lungs are associated with the Autumn Season

The element is Metal

The colour is grey/white

The sound is weeping

The odour is rotten

The emotion/energy is grief and sadness

The function of this organ is the regulation of our life-giving network which stems from our respiration.

The associated organ is the Large Intestine (Chapter 1)

A balanced Autumn provides the ability:

- to take in the richness of life

- to feel loss and move on from the loss, rather than getting stuck in a perpetual, unresolved sense of loss

- to accept that when something is over, complete, then it is imperative that we let go

Behaviours that can become evident when the autumn/metal goes out of balance which we and others can sense in us are:-

Feeling/being nonchalant	to	being deeply moved
Feeling/being messy and polluted	to	craving quality and purity
Seeking connection	to	feeling cut off
Feeling overworked	to	feeling resigned / inert
Feelings of fragility	to	rigid / intransigent / dogged

Chapter 3

Discover your

Kidneys

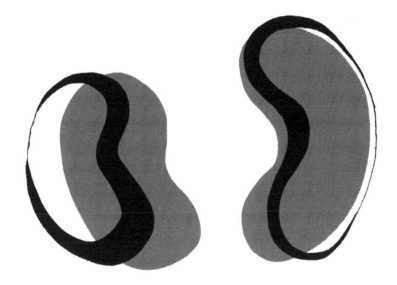

L'addition, s'il vous plait (The Bill please.)

Winter Season and Water Energy

Emotion: Anxiety/fear

This chapter is introducing you to our amazing KIDNEYS - that are responsible for the creation of power, skill and ability. They are the controller of fluid. Fluid - within our mind, body and spirit systems.

The Season is Winter which is associated with water. With fear being the emotion that our kidneys facilitate.

One of our body's brilliant alert systems is our ability to experience fear at differing levels.

Water's associated colour is blue.

According to Stuart Goldenburg, in May of 2014, "Our blue planet holds plenty of water, but only 2.5% of it is fresh. The amount of freshwater has fallen 35% since 1970, as ground aquifers have been drawn down and wetlands have deteriorated. Meanwhile, demand for water, intensive agriculture and energy is soaring. Overall water, demand is on pace to overshoot supply by 40% by 2030."

Does the above alert you? If it does, then your water energy and life force is working with you. If you also consciously want to start and continue to be a part of the solutions, then your kidneys are serving you in that seasonal energy within your own navigational system.

A balanced water energy within your clever body, your kidneys, notice danger and assess the risk that something or even someone presents. This aspect of your own energy system will be able to reassure you that you are safe or not, or if the planet also literally needs your input. When you are at risk you will be able to take action to protect yourself.

Taken to the ultimate level, your own life force can actually show you, just like the animals who, before huge natural disasters, go to higher ground, for instance. Mothers often know when their children are in danger and may not be anywhere near them at the time. Hunters traditionally, or now trackers in the wild, know exactly when danger is around. They can sense it in their "waters," or their bones, which are also associated with the kidneys.

In an ever changing energetic world where seasons, patterns and literal rhythms are affecting us, we can begin to see how we are also affecting everything around us. The more we get to know the dynamics of our own energy/ life force, and the more alive we can feel, the more present we can be to what is really going on collectively. Gradually, we can become less reactive and more active. As that happens, we are nourishing our kidney energy. I hesitate to use the word "balancing the water," for kidney energy for the following reason.

Initially, a truly alarming moment arrived when some bright spark in our class asked during my training in Integrated Chinese Medicine.

"What happens when we manage to get the patient's energy in balance and even?"

I think I will honestly remember to my dying day the expression of the teacher with her serene, amused smile when she knew damn well the impact her words would make, as eventually they would hit home to us.

This is the gloriously unsettling sentence that came out of her mouth:

"Well, as is the nature of all things, they then will get out of balance again."

Eventually a patient felt safe enough to spit out one day during treatment what I had known was her real and appalling terrifying circumstances. Her pulses, colouring and voice were constantly telling me. She had a groan that bubbled relentlessly on. Listening to her was like a babbling brook that was groaning and creaking under the weight of water relentlessly wearing it down.

Treatment had allowed her gradually to rebuild within her enough safety for her to tell her truth. I continued each and every time to be reassuring, to be a safe haven that consistently showed up for her week in, week out. I knew she was in grave danger so I had to deal with my own real and appropriate fear for her. I took advice from someone who was a supervisor to me and my work. I was already very familiar with domestic violence of the verbal but also of the physical kind.

It was very clear to me that this woman was being violated every single day and in every possible way. I had admired hugely her turning up to see me at all, and so resolutely. The kidneys do provide us with our will. Somehow she kept finding a way to turn up weekly with a way to pay also. She was having all her means taken but she still showed up and never asked for a discount. It would have insulted her to have me offer her one. This was her time, her gift to herself and something that she was rebuilding herself around, actually within her and not dependent on me. Very early on in treatment it is vital to establish what is going to be safe, appropriate and manageable on an on-going basis for a patient. Every aspect of caring for a patient's wellbeing in an integrated way has to be thought through. Finances and payments need to be tackled straightforwardly as it is one of the main blocks to people's sense of wellbeing. The flow of resources is much more about our energetic systems than we initially are taught or realise.

Initially she had not come about her domestic situation, and was so unaware that it was the root of her deep seated wound. Her childhood's familiarity with nothing but vicious, cruel violence was still living and vibrating in her own body. So, *unintentionally*, *unconsciously*, and certainly *innocently*, she was an open wound energetically emitting a frequency for another damaged and violent abuser to come along. Unconsciously she had recognised the familiar and with a major imbalance in her kidney energy she had not recognised the danger of getting involved with this man. He literally smelt familiar to her, so she mistakenly thought she was going home.

The good news about this way of beginning to understand this, is also accepting, how clever our bodies are, as they will keep magnetising towards us the very things that need to be resolved. We are actually in our greater wisdom and energetic truths being a constant antenna to the real possibilities of vibrant integrated health.

The familiar must never be underestimated; it will always be like a beacon that comforts in and of itself, no matter how dangerous or, seemingly from the outside, outrageously confusing it is to others. Ultimately, I understand that it is an overriding mechanism that propels us to return to scenes of unfinished business within us. So, for instance, where we have been robbed perhaps of our innocence when we were too young to know differently, we actually sometimes find that we return to an equally abusive situation to excavate ourselves, to find the innocence and energy to become transformed by finding the strength to recognise the truth. We are freed by the greater and more familiar within us ultimately.

The kidney energy is also connected to ancestral energy and often untapped resources. It is possible for one person to push back generations of abuse, to find the truth of all that suffering, to disarm it and walk away from abuse strengthened and empowered, having totally disarmed the bully within the abuser by seeing and hearing abuse for what it is.

Oddly, for what was going on inside of my patient, she was actually quite intimidating with an underlying agitation all of the time. In fact, if you saw her, she would have come across as having her 'shit together'. To others, her aura might even have seemed soothing and calm. She was so in control of everything that she did indeed appear calm and yet only with training was I able to see, feel and sense the agitation.

The day arrived for her babbling brook to spit out the enormous boulder that was in the way of the brooks flow, and had been squeezing its way either side of her own banks. So in all ways, metaphorically, literally and energetically her own tectonic plates were shifting, her own waters rising.

Unfortunately, we all remember what it was like the day we heard, then saw, the consequences of the tectonic plates shifting in Japan and earlier in Indonesia. Shifting plates and rising water caused a massive and devastating loss of lives, livelihoods, homes and much more, the consequences of which have continued. So as a practitioner you know that is coming in your patient so you need to be willing to hold very steady, clearing away everything to the higher grounds, to know that they can recover. Not just recover but be that much stronger for what has been and is devastating still while it has a hold on the patient's energy.

"I am raped every night I now suddenly realise. Against my will, he never asks and will even barge into my bathroom if he decides he wants his fix. I am his property as is everything else."

She babbled it out so quickly I could so easily have actually missed entirely the enormity of what she was suddenly able to spit out. I waited each week though not to miss it and treated particular points to make it come to the surface.

"I had not realised that 'no' does not exist in my world with him so I am beginning to realise the terrible danger that I am in , and particularly now as I begin to want to protect myself and take action."

Like many before her, I then was in the position to make safety precautions for her. In many other cases that are hauntingly similar but perhaps have slightly different manifestations it is important to wait before making suggestions, even when you know someone's life is in danger. It is so easy to make things far more dangerous and worse. Becoming a third energetic dynamic in an already fraught dangerous situation is a tightrope walk, anyway. I had been waiting for her energy to be built back enough in her own system for her to come to terms with her own truth, and then also face the consequences of her situation getting actually worse before it could get better.

We collectively live in such a quick fix society and certainly not one that wants to have anything get worse before it gets better. Seemingly perhaps we have so lost touch with our natural world that we are becoming more and more afraid of the actual real cycles of life. A student in our class asked what was meant by the statement, "water is the great leveller."

Again a hugely respected teacher answered: "Water always gets its way eventually, even over time it will erode the toughest materials on this planet, so never under or overestimate the water-the will within people. The excess, hindrance, or lack of water equally will cause total and absolute devastation left to its own relentless ways. Work with its full power and authority within people and in the universe, never believing that you will ever be able to tame it ferocity.

"You all will be in the privileged positions of appearing often to be magicians; but according to your levels of real humility, though, will you be truly good practitioners. Bringing patients home to themselves to master their own seasons. The will of the water element is to allow people to find ways through the toughest of situations. As they evolve ever more consciously and energetically you will be able to connect them to all the possibilities to not pay the prices of others unconsciousness. To even get to the point where your patients will be harnessing the S.H.I.T that does happen to strengthen and not dwindle their internal resources."

I had so wanted to call this book. **S**imple **H**ealth **I**ntegrated **T**ogether - S.H.I.T. happens. As it is only through each cycle of what does keep happening that we get to master our own energetic systems. This patient was indeed getting her life together but through the cycles, not by avoiding any of them.

"Groundwater is like your savings account. It's okay to draw it down when you need it, but if it's not replenished, eventually it will be gone." Matt Roddell, Goddard, Chief of the Hydrological Sciences Laboratory, NASA Goddard Space Flight Center.

That day, we organised for the patient to entrust a friend with a packed bag of essentials if the time came for her to leave. We even

80

went to the lengths of having a second passport delivered to another address as her husband had her passport under lock and key. We used stealth, discretion and careful planning to work around her reality as step by step she decided what she wanted to do. Her very own passport was lost to her, even though agonisingly for her own freedom she slept with a copy of it under the roof that she slept in, in daily terror, as well as very nasty physical symptoms that no amount of antibiotics was going to resolve.

It is sobering to know how many people are either without a passport at all or are in similarly enslaved positions.

Gradually, she started to really see this man for the broken, sick bully he was, who now she did not want to rescue, recognising that it was not her job to wait to see if he ever changed. Whilst her own mental and physical health remained in danger, her only perspective became saving herself with the realisation that her husband would not necessarily ever change. By her very presence and behaviour she was actually colluding with the unacceptable, as she had sadly learnt that it was the safer option whilst she had been living in isolation with his abuse. It was very tricky to impose that sense to her until she herself came to those very personal assessments as daily her life depended on her conforming to his sickness to a certain extent.

She even had ended up accepting very unacceptable behaviour from her very spoilt bullying children, all of whom colluded with the verbal abuse as if it was normal. Sadly it had become their norm.

She now saw that she wanted to rescue herself and find a life where she would be able to replenish. We talked through the homework I gave her so that she would not be caught out by him sensing instinctively that he was losing control of her. I taught her as much as I was able to, to start sensing when his abuse would start. Knowing that the day would come when she would become more afraid of staying than of venturing into the total unknown, as suddenly an outcast in her particular level of society. She would not be supported for saying "no" to a cultural undercurrent of bullying. We both knew that she would be rejected by many. Her husband would manipulate even what remained of her own family that had colluded with the abuse from her childhood. So as she gathered perspective, trust and was able to be reassuring to herself, she also began to actually be excited. She felt very soothed by being able to face realistically what the changes were likely to bring. Her drive for such a huge shift was building.

The excitement of her regaining her own inner authority, will and life force was highly motivating to her. She also knew he would not want to lose face or control so he almost certainly would come after her. I asked her if she felt safe enough to take the risk of taping how he talked to her for just three days and then to put the recorder in her luggage out of the house. We lined up support for her legally and emotionally so that when the day came - and it did - she left and never looked back.

Eventually, she got her divorce and her freedom, so much so she found herself doing what she loved and fell in love, living happily and peacefully. She has never had to see her husband again and no one ever was able to abuse her again on any level. Even letting go of her two children who sided totally with her husband. He held the purse strings and although adult they wanted to stay in the drama and battle zone that again was familiar to them. We both knew that to love her children was one thing but to like them was very different. She faced honestly that she not only did not like their behaviour but that she did not miss the terrible bullying dramas that they were also a part of. They both were hooked on "so called social drug taking", but as she realised quickly upon leaving neither of them yet were ready to make any changes. She grieved all the hopes, dreams and expectations that were clearly not going to come about with them.

Her situation was relatively extreme as it was within the confines of a very gilded and high profile life that her husband led. She had, though, presented me with the following symptoms that were debilitating and frightening her, although initially in a rather detached way:

- a sore and aching back that worsened at night which was generally when her husband would come home and want sexual gratification before he changed and went back out, increasingly leaving her alone.

- a dry throat and mouth at night

- night sweats

- tinnitus

- constipation with dry stools

- the beginning of oedema in her legs and sometimes loose stools out of the blue also

- her knees were cold to touch and she had noticed that they were beginning to feel weak and painful

- She was slightly blue under her eyes and around her mouth. Her husband demanded her be "perfect," so the oedema on her legs is what she really was alarmed about. Going out publicly to very grand affairs with her husband peacocking around with her was unnerving anyway without her now having to hide her legs, which he considered to be her best feature. So, her attempts to hide the swellings were beginning to cause more control and cruelty from her husband.

All of the above symptoms were stopped as her investment into herself began to pay dividends. She ended up with her new partner having the life that she had always dreamed of, traveling the world with an appropriate amount of risk assessments and using her potential more and more that gave her daily life joy, purpose and peace. Together, they weathered some nasty and unpleasant storms from others, with others' prejudices and imbalances. However, they saw them for what they were so they both did not get caught into a life of more reactivity. Almost no one from her old life ventured into her new one, and without the green eyed monster arriving. They were furious with her obvious happiness and delightful husband.

I have just taken a break whilst writing this and was chatting to a local where I live. Her friend, a busy consultant for Urology, was being ferried to and from the various hospitals that she currently worked at by a driver. With the levels of tiredness, they are not expected to drive themselves around, but merely to keep working on ill patients whose quality of lives they are involved with. That story is classically, for us as practitioners, one that is shouting out about an imbalance, in part, in the water, winter season.

As a society or societies now we are so out of touch with our natural resources. Within ourselves and, therefore, outside of ourselves, it is difficult for us to connect our own individual behaviour with what is happening outside of ourselves.

It is interesting to note that the Chinese have a traditional understanding that what they were and did was always a result of what had gone before them and how they behaved was always how the next generations would be affected. They had a real sense of the collective and not so much the individual. Now, most western societies have a dangerous notion of just ourselves, or of only our immediate family and friends. It is not a part yet of our collective consciousness the connection between our individual choices and actions and then therefore the consequences to the wider collective.

In a white paper that I feel honoured to be able to read:

"Draining the Groundwater "Bank": First Pictures and data of Imminent, Invisible Water Crises. 2014, discusses the state of our planet, and yet in the way we were trained, that also describes the patients that came to me. A few notable quotes:

"Groundwater is like your savings account. Its okay to draw it down when you need it, but if it's not replenished, eventually it will be gone," Matt Roddell, Goddard, Chief of the Hydrological Sciences Laboratory, NASA Goddard Space Flight Center.

"It's like taking money out of your bank account without knowing how much money is in your bank account. It's a really terrifying prospect," Kate Voss, policy fellow, UC Center for Hydrologic Modeling, UC Irvine.

It was my job to assess whether patients were doing exactly the above on every level and in fact not registering any fear, at least consciously.

Another example of the water element in a human becoming parched:

> "My teeth are all beginning to wobble and I am getting fewer erections which are somewhat flaccid."

After my patient found out that he could say almost anything to me and that I was not going to judge him, he was so relieved to tell me really what was disturbing him.

Having asked him extensively about his erections and sex drive, he was only too relieved to sum up what was burning up inside him without the shame, embarrassment or humiliating titterlations. Locker boy jibes that are so expected and almost certainly delivered around the actual agonies of our suppressed and limited national contexts of our sexualities.

He was not yet at a point, however, that he was going to feel comfortable enough talking to me about his overwhelming and all-consuming addiction, as described in Western terms, but in Integrated Chinese Medicine we would only describe his behaviour in terms of his energetic patterns.

He would have been convinced, if asked, that the profound noise in his own head and the burning heat in his groin was not noticeable on the outside, whilst all of the time wondering how he could get his next sexual fix.

He was not to know that I had just put the phone down to another patient who was worried about her little boy. The relevancy to her having chosen to have IVF treatments for her last child would not have been in her mind and in part connected to what she was telling me about her little boys 'willy fetish' as she was describing it.

"Wherever we go and whatever we are doing it is very embarrassing. I mean even in the supermarket, he is taking his tiny willy out and playing with himself. It's not normal"

I had taken a calculated risk with her energy, tone and spirit on the phone.

"Well, it's certainly behind closed doors how many grown men behave."

She giggled and relaxed a little.

"Bring him in and we will settle his energy so that he will stop trying to get himself back into an energetic balance. It is very clever of him. Thank you for ringing me."

This dear little chap who was barely old enough to walk was instinctively trying to rebalance his system. Unintentionally, he was paying the bill, *l'addition s'il vous plait,* for his parents' choices. There is no judgment, but there are ongoing consequences to children born through IVF, and very often the mother also pays a heavy price for her choices, too.

So, in fact was the male patient who I had in front of me describing his erection as 'somewhat flaccid'. At times like this it is almost impossible to not burst into fits of laughter, simply because of the choice of words used. Not such a great way though to build trusting rapport. He was paying a huge bill for how burnt out his system was. He had been working in a system of competitive work where he was encouraged to play hard, using cocaine and alcohol as a normal part of his days, whilst working long, over adrenalised days continually.

He was so out of balance that it was not occurring to him to get anything fixed apart from what he thought was fixing him seven to ten times a day. I was trained and very familiar with all levels of addictions, so recognising the signs of someone being driven by a relentless inferno, which no amount of sexual release was going to quench, was possible for me to pick up. Also his pulses were showing me very clearly that every single time he was having a momentary sexual release, he was further emptying his own precious resources, which was making the problem worse. The fact that his hearing was going also or that his memory was slightly beginning to fail was of no alarm to him. He was in no way picking up on any of the feedback mechanisms that his own body was giving him.

No wonder every single religion and philosophy on this earth and through the ages has taught that to "know ourselves is of the utmost importance". We all have this unbelievably ingenious feedback going on all the time. We are literally driving around in our own vehicles with a large panel that bleeps and lights up, as in cars these days telling us what to be alert to.

So, danger was knocking on my patient's door on many integrated levels. He could not detect it as he was so caught up in the vicious cycle of desperate energetic and physical, chemical, let alone mental, emotional turmoil. All of his relationships were in shreds, which he was still caught up in believing was "to do with them," and certainly not connected in any way to his own behaviour. He had learned to be very seductive and charismatic in his intense desire and need to get what his body was demanding so dangerously. There was no other space or room as his body chemistry was now running his own vehicle.

A powerful quote that I had come across in my ongoing studies summed up this character in front of me:

> "The art of seduction can impede all forms of real and safe intimacy."

His only survival tool left was seduction. Inevitably like so many of our survival mechanisms they usually have a shorter shelf life than we realise. We get comfortably soothed by the familiarity of a behaviour that seems reliable, until suddenly it does not.

The first three treatment sessions were spent showing him by my actions that none of his usual antics with others would work on or around me. If I did not manage to build a safety net for him in the context of a treatment space, then I was going to fail him.

It was unlikely that I was going to be able to suggest verbally the real and lasting actions that he would be able to do to really shift the probability of him having a stroke or heart attack. He was almost on the edge already so I had to work fast if I was going to succeed in shifting him out of the danger that he did not know he was in; telling him straight was not going to work. As a practitioner, you learn fast the extreme limits of language and the incredible art and strengths of action/energy over words. Actions speaking louder and lasting longer often, particularly when it comes to people's energetic health.

Fundamentally, within his energy bank he had spent his one-time inheritance; he was actually bankrupt and was on the verge of losing his actual home, in the sense that his body was his primary home.

Sometimes being a practitioner is an alarming and lonely responsibility, as I was, in that instance, in a position to know where he was heading, which was straight to appalling suffering that his body would not have the energy to come back from. He had used up any spare juice he had, so no wonder his erections were "flaccid."

I had been in practice long enough to know damn well that I could not speak to his doctor, for instance, as very often we, in those days, were considered with great suspicion, or perhaps as practising something that sorted out headaches or perhaps stress only.

It still seems to be too disorientating for most people to believe that there has been a very sophisticated medicine that has been around for over 5000 years. Which if, integrated with the incredible strengths of Western Medicine, that has been around for 100 to 150 years, would be providing more solutions easily available to the masses.

Even now, the natural means that proper doctoring requires is being stripped and replaced by machines and drugs. So, I often would try to work out possible scenarios where I would pull in more support for a patient attempting to head off at the pass trouble that was so clearly brewing. Often, though, patients came to me having exhausted the usual roots, so sending them back again to their doctors I knew already would mean more stress for them. To be any good as a practitioner, you have to know the limits and strengths of what you can offer and equally the same with the system that is considered to be top dog at the moment in the West. You have to be very aware of circumnavigating the stress and strain of the systems that are already causing your patients a sense of powerlessness. As we in Integrated Chinese Medicine are taught in a system that is fundamentally preventive in all of its actions it becomes second nature for us to see, hear and also smell in the winds what is on its way next for a patient or in fact a system.

Years ago, working alongside the Western medical system, as it was being insidiously taken over by the seduction of the "big pharma," it was easy to see that a state of national medical bankruptcy would arrive, which as I write is upon us with more cancers, diabetes and inflammatory disorders now overwhelming an already overburdened system. We were headed towards burning up our own water element and on more levels than one back then.

We have so polluted our waters that there are endless written papers from many on the medical kickbacks or bills that are being paid by the younger generations. The hormones we have pumped into women without really knowing the long term side effects are now affecting the next generations of young people who are drinking water that has been so treated that it in no way represents what its original state needs to be.

With the patient in front of me at that time, I was trained to see what lay ahead of him. There was a lot I might be able to do for him if I could bypass what he was energetically wired to sabotage every single week. I asked him if he was willing to come to see me three times each week for three weeks at the end of his working days. He agreed and got used to falling asleep before I had even finished putting needles in him. I chose to ask him to come at the end of his days as I knew also that his kidney energy would be at its lowest so his burning need for a fix would be at its strongest, but if he quickly got used to energetically being quenched by the treatment instead, then I might be able to break the appalling cycle he was in that was rapidly spiralling completely out of control. He had no idea that I needed to be on to every single detail of what his energy was telling me. His life depended on my knowledge and at this point his lack of self-awareness. Absolutely no pressure then!

After each session I introduced another tiny change for him to make and kept re enforcing the ones that I had to carefully monitor. Knowing that patients who do not know themselves well will not answer questions accurately, it is up to us to be such good detectives that we can assess what is the literal truth, with then the backing of the body's clever language that speaks loudly to us. Respectfully, we need to access as much information as is necessary to make life changing treatments possible and accurate. He was so grateful to be coming off the effects of what we call empty heat, adrenalised highs and lows that he was very willing. He also did not feel threatened yet as I had not tackled in words what was really going on. He would not have had any reason to suspect that I not only did know what was really going on, but was already treating the real underlying causes. In order to treat what he had come to me about it was impossible to not keep aiming at what we call the "roots" of signs and symptoms.

In the fourth week, I asked him if he was interested in learning about how to rebuild his energy through mastering his sexual desires. Instantly his hackles went up with a curious alertness, with simultaneous immediate animosity. He almost became aggressive in the instant defended state that I had triggered in him.

If you watch all of the marvellous animal programmes, you will know the incredible interplays that take place between animals of all sorts as they go through the rituals of survival. Very often I do not have a clue which animal is going to come out still intact, let alone alive. At that point I was instantly reminded of those programmes, honestly wondering if I would not have preferred to be in my own home, relaxing and reading a good book. In fact, almost anything except playing a practitioner that was doing her level best in a truly terrifying situation as another's person life was within my means to alter and perhaps influence in saving.

I knew that he could and would be vile, dishonest and very unpleasant indeed if I mishandled this next move. He was capable of having a journalist write lies about me and ruin my practise within days.

"I have had lots of patients that are really enjoying working with this great guy who teaches them ancient ways of becoming stronger and stronger and much more virile through some breathing techniques that may interest you," I said as casually and nonchalantly as I could muster at that time.

My heart rate felt as if my heart was springing out of my mouth as if on a sprung coil. He sat straighter; the energy in the room went electric as he peered at me with a brutal momentary force. Like a ticker tape across his brain I could see that he was deciding if I knew more than I had let on. It was a professional uncomfortable judgment call to behave as if, no, I did not. So, I attempted to have my face be neutral and inquiring. I stilled myself with techniques that I have learnt to do whilst having mostly vile procedures done to me, or in hammering scanners waiting for evidence of the next need for immediate surgeries.

These moments of raw shifts were taking place in slow time when time itself really does seem to stop. I knew that however initially alert I had been that I could tip the balance by being very solid about my clear intention. It really is one of the many moments in a treatment room with Integrated Chinese Medicine that you are practising energetic spiritual kung Fu with your breath, your movement, your intent, your knowledge with also your acceptance of your limits.

I never went into the treatment room without embracing all that I do not know, being willing to step aside, whilst firmly believing that there is literally hanging in the ether a giant library. A library that if I really get out of the way I can and do gain information from, enabling me to be a bridge to the patient's next level of potential.

A grunt from him, diffused the atmosphere as he relaxed:

"How does that work then?"

Phew. The moment of danger for us both was over.

He did not have a heart attack and did learn to master his own sexual energy, even managing to replenish his internal resources a little. As his own energy grew, he became aware of his own warning light system. One day a year later, he walked in and told me he had resigned from his job and that it was the best decision of his life. He also had very clear plans of what he was going to do but taking into consideration his own integrated needs, no longer run by extreme need and desperation.

He was no longer paying the bill for systems that he decided didn't work for him. Importantly, those around him were no longer paying bills for his behaviour and his out of control imbalanced sexual appetites.

As he was able to stop paying the bills for the system that he had not had the knowledge to handle, bills that he then passed on to others with his out of control behaviour, stopped.

He was even learning to be intimate with one woman and allowing himself to have some support with an excellent therapist who was really taking him through some of the vital steps of maturing that he had bypassed completely. His only reference ever to me to anything that had really been in his main complaint was when he said,

"I'm not sure I can believe it myself, but I'm enjoying being faithful and not cricking my neck every time a skirt goes past. Also, I'm not totally sure why its connected but somehow it is. My resources on all levels are being restocked. I was always not having enough, even if I made shit loads of money it was never enough. I was always getting clobbered by my own stupidity and then also others. Money was like water that just ran straight through my fingers. You wouldn't believe the bills and tabs that others would just expect me to pay. The daft thing was, I did. I was far too scared not to. Even my boss would put all his drinks on my tab in the local wine bar. I never confronted him or took it to the accounts department to put it down as something else to get reimbursed. Now, not only do I notice, but I just don't run around like the arsehole I was. Thanks for that. I don't get it but I know it's these treatments. Those Chinese know a thing or two don't they about the body and its real capacity?"

The next chapter brings in the link up with your bladder which works alongside the kidneys in the Water element.

Questions to Ask Yourself
Tantalising teasers for glamorous living

Here is something to think about involving paying bills that are not yours directly or necessarily the ones that you want to, at least, unconsciously. The real question to ask yourself regularly is: are you 'paying' attention to the quality of your daily life force and energy?

Are you aware at all that you have an emergency account of reserved energy that actually cannot be replenished once used up? You really do have a reserve tank, with some people having a bigger reserve tank than others, but once it has gone your very life force becomes, what I call, thin.

How do you reassure yourself, and are you aware of needing a lot of reassurance or are you aware of how many risks you take which others do not and would not?

What do you do to keep yourself safe, and who and how do you trust others?

If your history has shown you that you are a lousy chooser of trustworthy friends, or accountants, for instance, what would you be willing to do to ensure that you accept others' input when choosing your next lover, for instance if you were looking for a longer term situation? Of course if a friend had proved their reliability in the first place that is to support you in different choices.

How lacking in personal drive are you? Do you carry projects through or do you start something and then leave it hanging mid-job or starting a project with no impetus to continue? Are you willing to seek help with completing jobs?

Whilst doing a job are you constantly smoking anxiously or are you incessantly cleaning for instance with no real awareness of what is driving you or your behaviour?

Are you using wisely and cleverly the opportunities that life is constantly bringing to your door, or are you wittering them away, only seeing your imagined dangers? Equally are you going through life dangerously unaware of the real dangers of your behaviour?

Sexual activity and over use of sex is very much the domain of the Water element. So are you having sex with numerous partners, unaware of why and what you are trying to fix within yourself? Are you dangerously having multiple partners without any protection for yourself or your partner, but just going for the 'rush' of the moment and to hell with the consequences?

Are you pushing yourself too hard all of the time, unaware of how unavailable that is making you for what you might also be saying that you want?

How much of your time is taken up in an underlying agitation that actually paralyses you? Are you willing to do something about it?

Whilst the kidney gives you, when in balance, a calmness and an ability to even refuel in silence, to replenish in the hibernating energy of the winter, the bladder which is the next chapter, talks about how you can gain cleverness - the cleverness to, on all levels, store fluids and excrete water through transformation.

This is an aside but so important if you do not already know this. Please be careful around plastic bottled water. It is now being confirmed that most cancers have traces of plastic in them so we are all digesting plastics insidiously. One way is through plastic heated or altered by direct sunlight so if at all possible be mindful around bottles in your cars or out in a room where sunlight is on the bottle.

Summary of the Kidneys chapter

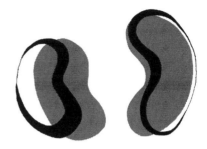

Kidneys

The Kidneys are associated with the Winter Season

The element is water

The colour is blue

The sound is groaning

The odour is putrid

The emotion/energy is fear/anxiety

The function of this organ is the creation of power. Our skill and ability stem from them.

The associated organ is the bladder (Chapter 4)

A balanced Winter provides the ability:

- Notice danger, assessing the extent of risk being presented
- Take action to deal with risks in appropriate ways
- Provide reassurance about safety

Behaviours that can become evident when the Winter energy is out of balance within us. These are the extremes that we may sense in ourselves or others.

Intimidating	to	reassuring
Driven	to	no drive
Taking risks	to	being over cautious/ imagining the worst
Distrusting	to	overly trusting

Chapter 4

Discover your

Bladder

Burdens of Carelessness

The Bladder is associated with the emotion: Fear/Anxiety

FEAR when not free to be expressed in genuine proportion to what is happening, ends up creating what I now term, burdens of carelessness.

CLAUSTROPHOBIC PATIENT - Was printed in big red letters right across an important medical document about me.

"I AM NOT". I did try so hard to contain my frustration, indignation and fear. I even managed to calm my voice right down mid raised shout. It had been a long week of no one seemingly taking on board the levels of unacceptable pain I was in with the total lack of care from the very group that are supposed to do just that. Please excuse the capitals, it is exactly what the burdens of carelessness promotes endlessly now in so many places, routinely, in our societies.

The routine carelessness though can become a great way of being in your human exercise gym. where beginning to manage one's own responses to the utter madness that is all around is a clever choice. The bladder gives you access to being clever.

I literally will line myself up to make most phone calls now so that I am as non-reactive as is possible with practise. Practise is what is needed if you are to keep any dignity and not begin to routinely sound like your part of a black adder script.

WHY was it vital that I got it removed you may ask .

Any inaccuracy that distracts the consultants and nursing staff from paying attention to the very severe issues that can kill me in a heartbeat is dangerous. There was a very high risk that I would be whisked into hospital very soon again. So I asked the admin department, politely by then as I managed to stuff down the fear, lower my voice, unclench my fist around the receiver and **breathe**, "why was it being written when I do not suffer from, as well, claustrophobia?".

"Well most of our patients do, so we put it on any way ." she replied tartly.

'Oh so asking us whether we do and writing down our answers does not make any difference then.' I thought in my head and just stopped myself from spitting out.

The admin department or at least this woman was not going to get it. What frightened and alarmed me was that she did not want to get it. I knew I was at a roadblock which I needed to circumnavigate my way through.

Few, admin folk do get the real consequences of what their actions are these days. They are way over stretched and in such overwhelm that their humanity gets spat out. One consultant I had to see is so protected that we are not allowed to know the administrators names and their office work is being done by a faceless business that does not cater for the human factor at all. It was terrifying the first time I encountered it. I ended up feeling and indeed being almost fined over some awful misunderstanding. Which literally only happened as the system that is now in place to backup this high flying consultant does not know how to divert from a script. Thank God I knew him well and had a good rapport so literally demanded that the correspondence was immediately sent to him. I got an apology and BUPA International was not charged for what had not happened. I would not accept the unacceptable. I was too well aware that so often people are too busy or patients too sick to be able to chase down such carelessness.

Now that so much medical things are paid for by the Insurance companies or the NHS, patients very rarely get to see what is actually happening with costs or even the administration. I have had such a lifetime of really now seeing the 'burdens of carelessness' being passed on to patients and certainly not really helping the truly great consultants that there are. I would even dare to say that the systems in place at present   actually support the inadequate and inefficient consultants. Illness is sadly very big business. When Western Medicine becomes so burdened with the unacceptable costs of what has now become the normal way of diagnosing and then supposedly treating patients the system will remain in place. Whilst failing more patients than anyone collectively realizes as there are such invested interests in keeping this giant Elephant in the room. Shoot me down in flames after you have really done your research about what I am talking about. Do not get me wrong either, I am very grateful to some aspects of Western Medicine but as an institute now it has seriously lost its way and does systematically fail patients. Until it becomes interested in the roots of disease it will remain so and therefore will be so often laying 'burdens of carelessness' in its wake, every which way, on patients.

I cannot force what I have to be clear about, on systems that do not want to be clear. Except when my life depends on it and then I will use the full power of the water element to be very clear with my will. In the muddle a lot of fudging can hide a lot of unnecessary mistakes. If occasionally a mistake is picked up on, some poor person takes the rap, then is scapegoated for what is a systemic problem.

I should know on numerous counts. Firstly as a practitioner working with so many patients who arrived at my clinics devastated and lost having received the worst of what does and can happen in the lost and broken system. They often would be scapegoated and treated appallingly with absurdly rude assessments which only arrogance justifies. They arrived having taken on so much carelessness that they were bedraggled with, and then the belief that the sign, symptom or pain was not real and that perhaps they were mad, neurotic or hysterical.

"PLEASE I BEG YOU, listen to me, just listen to me. I am desperate and I need your help"

A stunning very thin elegant woman walked in and slumped in obvious despair, her raised voice briefly was from a total terror that hung like a thick fog in the room. Immediately I said

"OK I will do just that and not interrupt until you have finished. Tell me please, I want to hear and listen".

She slumped further having scanned my eyes first to see if I was honest and real. The dam within her had already gone way beyond the river banks, her flood was internally rampaging all through her. I rarely had ever come across such obvious and acute terror. She was clear and articulate with it.

"You see I know that I am dying. I so passionately don't WANT TO. I have two adopted children who have only just begun settling from such incredibly abusive beginnings and a husband that I adore. I have waited twenty years for my Mr Right. We were soul mates and met when we were on a foreign trip from both of our schools. After five days together we knew, even at the age of 15, that we wanted to spend the rest of our lives together. Life however got in the way, like it does and we only got together three years ago. I have been scanned twice and three consultants and four radiologists say they cannot see anything and therefore all my symptoms are coming from early menopause and hysteria. I know I have a brain tumour. Why will they not believe me and not their machines? You have to believe me. I am dying and I don't have long left. They have even stopped asking me if my symptoms are worsening, which of course they are."

Caught in the headlights this Bambi like creature appealed to every bit of me to believe her.

I did.

She sighed heavily relieved clearly to be held in respect and care. I made sure that she did not want to add anything and let the space be hers. It was the least I could do if someone is brave enough to tell you that they are dying and that they do not want to. In my career I have had far more patients telling me that they do not want to live.

"Will you let me take your pulses?" I asked. I went to her when she nodded, again deep in her utter turmoil of actually very appropriate terror. She was totally lucid, rational and terrified, not in the least bit hysterical.

I used everything that I had learnt then and there to send her body and spirit as much love and compassion that it was so easy to be feeling at a fellow human's extreme vulnerability, as I held her hands taking all twelve of her pulses. Sure enough out of several blocks that we can feel that indicate death she had all of them.

"I believe you"

Sitting up, clearly hugely relieved she almost smiled with the validation that meant that she was not mad as well.

"So what on earth do I do, I don't want to leave my children or husband?"

I sat in silence feeling and thinking my way into a response that would serve her properly and deeply.

"I hear you and I totally believe you, which I will keep validating for you. The big question is this, as you are dying and there may not be anything anyone can do, are you willing to come to terms with what you do have right now?" Not wasting a minute by wanting more than you have today and that you might have very little left of?"

"That has got my attention"

She snapped almost immediately out of the state of terror which frankly I had prayed might happen, equally there was a huge risk that I might frighten her further. Given the circumstances, I had to follow my gut instinct though.

"Oh I get it, you mean because I am right, what has been overwhelming me is not being heard and therefore not being able to make plans and look after things as best I can in time. I do believe that everything happens for a good reason ultimately so I must prepare my husband and children mustn't I.?"

"Yes"

"I want you to do two things which I will support you with, if that feels right for you. I want you to go back to the hospital and demand that they rescan you, and today. If you want me to come with you, I will or your husband must meet you at the hospital. Do you think you are ok to drive ?"

Again she looked into my eyes, tears dripped down her ashen face.

'You would come wouldn't you?"

I nodded, almost in tears myself. This woman's life force was already leaving her. The terror had almost fuelled her, so now as it evaporated with being validated she was going fast. We both knew that she was going to die, her time was here and not when she would have dearly loved it to be.

"No, you carry on treating as I know you have a full afternoon, your wonderful practise manager fitted me in as I BEGGED her. I will ring you later and let you know what is happening."

She left, thanking me with a huge hug as if we had been friends for ever. I shall never forget the dignity and grace with which she walked out of the clinic room.

I sobbed releasing some of her unshed tears and some of my own at so understanding that it was not so much the dying that was so disturbing. It was that when she needed care the most and validation she had had the opposite. Her children were to be robbed of their mother but they nearly were robbed of the completions that were in fact able to take place in the end.

Her husband rang me that night to again thank me, again treating me as if I was an old family friend. They had rescanned her and found a tumour that was already so huge they could not understand how it was possible for it to have been missed before. They were so appalled that she had driven herself to the hospital that they were again almost rude to her. She had asked that her husband tell me that as she had sensed that I would understand. I did and told him why she had wanted me to know. They operated immediately under suddenly huge intense drama but closed her up again telling her husband at 3 am that she would probably stay alive for a further 6 weeks. He kept me in touch until the end. With her very much at the helm the whole family was at peace unbelievably when the time came. They accepted what they knew they could not in this instance change. Even her two adopted children were prepared and so extraordinarily grateful at such an early age to have known what love was and for so long. In such contrast to their earlier experiences they were under no illusion about the real harshness of life.

The above is a good example of when to know how to not under or over use our will. The water, winter season is a time of building our reserves and cherishing our resources. If misspent it can lead us to over use our will which will lead to a deep seated exhaustion and burnout. This patient and I both knew that she was right, she was dying. My job was to accept that immediately so that I could serve her in doing the same. She needed to use what life force she had left to put her affairs in order.

The notion of the burdens of carelessness had come to me because of the very rare genetic syndrome that I was born with, that no one really understands. I have bumped up against the limits of the Western medical system my entire life, respecting what is to be respected and leaving the rest alone as far as is possible. It has been like walking through a minefield where I permanently am trying not to trip up fragile egos or arrogance that buffers fear. Again the paradox is that my personal experience ultimately has helped me to be a far better practitioner with my patients so it too has its amazing purposes.

Cleverness associated with the bladder is also balanced with the kidneys bringing in wisdom when your water is in balance. Wisdom compels you to withdraw from a situation when you can cleverly assess whether your longer term goals would be compromised by expelling willfulness, resources before the right time. The healthy functioning of the bladder is being able to keep your life force, your energy in check.

Where I lived once we had to have large water tanks that were constantly monitored to see what the levels were. They were vital to sustain life so it was a weekly ritual to check them and then taking immediate action if possible to do something to replenish them if they dipped below a certain level.

Bladder syndromes and patterns on a physical level revolve around mostly what we call damp heat or damp cold in the bladder. So difficult, burning, turbid, painful, frequent or urgent urination is just some of what I would be discovering about your bladder if you came knowing you had an issue with your bladder or urethra. So apart from establishing if you have had excess exposure to cold, damp, heat I would be establishing if having too much sex was an element in your full energetic picture. Setting jokes aside about never being able to have enough sex, some people are filling their emptiness up by excess sex. Excess according to not a moral judgement but literally what in fact a body can process.

Long term unresolved emotional problems are always something I would be looking at with this element also. In general ways there is a tendency now in our culture to be burning through our internal resources with no wisdom or cleverness to be seen. Our nervous systems, for example, are getting fried by electromagnetic resonances for which the effects are still being generally denied. Children are being put to sleep with TVs, computers and other equipment in their rooms. We are losing touch with the obvious wisdom of allowing ourselves silence, darkness and real stillness at night when our bodies are refreshing themselves.

The depletion of our resources leads to more anxiety and then a literal burning up of our internal and external energy, resources.

Interestingly many practitioners of Chinese Medicine right across

America reported a huge and sharp rise in bladder issues, with the equivalent of what is known as cystitis when Donald Trump became President. The patients were able to say how frightened they were and their bodies were displaying the fear. Very often patients would arrive after some terrible and frightening news with bladder symptoms.

An imbalance in your water can lead to being economical with the truth, almost as if not being truthful is a constant preparation for all the scary things that may happen. Equally lack of fear will lead you to underestimate the dangers, almost to the point of again not being wise or truthful. Accuracy to an imbalanced and overly, constant anxious mind is not necessarily a strong point. There is not a deep connection to any of the long term or even immediate consequences to living with the effects of a revved up engine, or system so over estimating a situation or under estimating either is also not picked up on.

One of my patients, after some while recovered sufficiently to stop coming to see me for the original issue he was so bothered about. He was an incredibly charismatic but disturbingly unpleasant man. He had been awarded very high honors and awards for heroism that he took very seriously indeed. He knew, from his perspective, that he was totally above the normal laws, manners or niceties of society. Having been held up to be so outstandingly brave he believed clearly that he was untouchable. His lack of fear was like being in a cage with a lion that you knew could and would pounce any minute. I remember having to put him very firmly in his place early on as he wanted to make mincemeat of me before he almost even walked through the treatment room. He bated everyone, I suspected for fun and malice, getting great pleasure out of being cruel, which no one ever dared, called him on as he was so highly acclaimed. From an Integrated perspective he was not so much brave as so totally out of balance that he had no fear. His lack of fear had worked for him and others in times of war and in his particular case seemingly he did not endanger others with his total inability to contemplate or wisely assess the danger signals. He had a putrid smell which no amount of heavy after shave and scent covered. He was very vain and simply took no notice of my request that on the first appointment he was not to use anything that had a smell to it.

Interestingly he had been given acupuncture from one of his batman in the war so he had great faith in it.

He was most put out by having frequent and urgent urine, feeling thirsty but not wanting to drink anything. He even had blood in his urine and would not go to his Doctor, who he called an idiot.

Almost funnily, the only time I saw him anxious was at the idea of going to a new doctor. He refused, completely confident that I would sort him out. Even the confidence though was an arrogant lack of fear. With treatment some of the very nasty baiting with the groaning in his voice did improve also.

I knew in my bones and deeply that he was a sexual predator trapping women and I suspect men also in his dreadful manipulating, controlling charisma. He was literally so 'polluted 'in his waters. He would have got me caught also if he could have. Trapped in a horrific mess that he would not have thought through for a second the danger my career would have been in. I would have been just another notch in his warped mind. He was challenged with his interest peaked as I clearly was not giving him any openings for his foul smelling water to spill dangerously into my work or personal life. He was only interested in me personally and sexually as he was convinced that he could change my mind. 'No' for him was just the beginning of him knowing that he had his prey where he needed them. I had no intention of being his next prey. Often during treatment he would put his slightly reptilian eyes on to me asking me a deliberately inappropriate question.

He had arrived in my clinic after quite some time of clinical practise so I was able to handle him in ways that worked for me and did not leave me crushed by the force of his 'waters'. I was also sufficient in balance myself to assess the dangers properly. Never once did he come to the clinic without the practise manager and I making sure she had my back and was physically present. Refusing to treat him would have been like a game for him so interestingly I had to use my Water energy to be wise and clever with him. Remaining consciously meticulous in my professional conduct, my manners, treating what I was able to treat and allow him to become sufficiently bored by the total lack of a game or a chase. I kept command by telling him when he next appointment was which was early in the day when I was sure I would have stronger energy.

Knowing that I would have been able to do a certain amount over time with his underlying imbalance I had to assess the energy that it took from me and my practise manager to make sure that we did not slip up at all with him. Thinking about the whole practise and all the other patients who deserved equal attention I used the water, bladder and kidney energy to assess the dangers of keeping this man as a patient. The burdens of carelessness did not need to be poured onto my other patients or the other practitioners with their patients. As it was my practise I took seriously the responsibilities I had to everyone. He was so potentially dangerous that it would not take much for him to charm his way into one of the other patients bedrooms. So in fact the practise manager and I even went to the lengths of making sure the treatments sessions were when there were less other patients waiting in the reception area.

Years after I had treated him I saw an article about him by a very brave journalist who did question the motives of his so called bravery. Having interviewed him very perceptively he had got to grips with what was really going on.

A lack of balance can lead to very subtle and controlling behaviour if it is coming from an imbalance in the water, bladder energy, simply because of the anxiety going on all of the time. This would be the other side of the spectrum in the water-winter energy. A person can be exhausting themselves with the perceived fears and danger of every possible event. They do not feel safe so often they are seeking safety in their control outwardly when in fact the inward lack of safety has to be resolved.

A patient I had would describe how anxious she got before her Chemo treatments so would be crying, "whimpering" (her words) beside her husband as he drove her to the hospital. As if she was not in the car he would take her mobile phone, answer calls, putting it on loud speaker and saying on being asked how she was by personal close friends who wanted the truth.

"Yes, yes she is doing just amazingly. So brave, hardly ever mentioning how frightening it must be. I have given her advice though about how to handle the whole situation and I must say she seems to be taking it all very well. Clearly my advice has been invaluable."

She was very funny in telling me about this, as she realised it routinely was happening particularly when she was feeling rough, vulnerable or would be just needing to let go a bit and not be so 'upbeat or positive'. She was also very resigned to him taking credit for making up scenarios where he made out that he was giving her advice. The more anxious he became the more he made up stories that were not even remotely true. Once she had got over the annoyance of such inaccurate chatter she began to realize how he was acting out his acute fear. She also began to realize that whilst he could not be in control or charge of her treatments he could be of her immediate surroundings. She said that his anxiety had hugely improved with treatments, so much so she had a sense that he would not have even been able to come to be with her beforehand. She said to me one day that she was convinced that he would have had a "very important " trip or business deal to have to handle at the very time that she would have liked him to be around before he had embarked on the treatments with her.

When working with family members from the same family or a married couple each interaction was very sacred as, in some ways each person was entrusting me with the realities of the nitty gritty of their relationships. They knew I would not repeat, without their permission anything to the other person. It was though incredibly helpful information always to help me support the marriage or family energetically as far as was possible.

Before we talked about her husband's anxiety this is what had lead to it.

"Why on earth does he do it, why he can't just tell my friends the truth I just don't get? I then feel mad as well as frightened and miserable?"

Her husband was a patient of mine and in fact had sent his wife to me.

So we were able to talk about his terrible underlying anxiety that no matter how she tried to soothe him would never last, she had observed.

"No amount of money would be enough when I know we have more than enough for almost every sort of eventuality. Our net worth is so vast now I am embarrassed by his poverty stance. I am so aware that most people would give anything to have even one percent of what we are blessed to have. So whilst I really appreciate what he has on one hand cleverly done, on the other I am anxious that we will never get to enjoy time together actually enjoying the life that money can buy, as he always thinks it is not enough. Funny really, or not so, as now it is my life that is threatened which no amount of money will help save me if my time is up. At least he is being with me right now. "I love him, but my God he is so controlling and annoying sometimes." She giggled with deep affection.

I continued to treat both these two as in fact the woman was able to recover, her husband began to slow up as he had had such a fright at the thought of losing his wife.

He even began to take very seriously what he did with his anxiety that previously he had not been aware of. He went three times a week to someone who literally taught him how to breathe deeply and then to do a breathing meditation where he was taken into his whole body to learn how to replenish himself through breath. He stopped being so driven. As a surprise for his wife he bought her the house she had always dreamed of having abroad and presented it to her for her 60th birthday present, topping it with him semi retiring.

They both learnt to really listen to each other at a level that they realised they had never done before. On their request one day I saw them both together as they wanted to know how the overlay of the others energy and energetic states was in some ways hindering their evolving. I showed them through mime, which ended up in us all roaring with laughter. They really got that they were out of rhythm literally from old belief systems that just did not work for who they both were and how much love there really was in their marriage. Fear had been the third person in their marital bed for too long.

We all know, at least, one person around us who is considered so kind or nice that it is often that same person who everyone assumes will take on the burdens that no one else can be bothered to take on. We all will participate in burdening that person unaware of the reasons why they keep saying yes or more likely are not able to say no.

We really do live in a society where we do not generally know our own yes or no. Our communication skills are still based so much on a real and underlying anxiety of how we will be judged and therefore will we be allowed still into the un-said club formations that we are brought up in. There is a fine web of club rules that are not ever talked about, which instinctively we perceive so we all lie most of the time. From being asked how we are and answering with directly dishonest answers mostly or constantly giving the other the information that we think they want. Hence the muddles of others forever saying yes when they actually mean no and vice versa. The water element always makes me think of this as, like the truth, water always has its way. Hence if we do not bother or even know how to bother about the details of our precious lives we do endlessly ask of others to carry the burdens. The truth always come out and usually in a torrent of water like eruptions that shock everyone. The 'damn' of lack of truthful communication will find its way to the surface. Disease comes in many forms, often it is all the unsaid communications that we were too afraid to express or simply did not know how to in ways that would not make more issues for us. The art of communicating successfully is a very tricky and long standing tool to learn.

One of the amazing things about becoming aware of your own water element, your own kidneys and bladder is that you will become much more conscious of what you are asking of yourself, therefore others. Only then will you begin to stop burdening others with your own carelessness.

Unglamorous tips for glamorous living or tantalizing teasers for your water season

Be aware of your own water gauges literally and figuratively .Start monitoring your water intake of clean, ideally not water that is full of fluoride (so bother to check your local water content }. Invest in knowledge about water filters.

Always drink it at room temperature; otherwise you are imposing on your body more work. Iced drinks are by nature cold forming to your system that does not respond well, when functioning at its optimum to cold temperatures.

Never hang around in cold damp and wet swimming costumes. It is really worth buying several pairs of whatever you like wearing and just get into the habit of changing after swimming, not waiting for the sun to dry you. Your bladder and kidneys will thank you.

Do not wander around on tiles without shoes on. The water, energy lines are connected to your feet so allowing what we would call damp or cold energy to flow up your legs through your feet is asking for trouble, if not immediately then later. So do not be complacent. Little children love kicking off their shoes and in fact it is frightening as a parent if they are in sliding slippers on surfaces. Where and when possible find a way of not allowing them to have bare feet when inside, for instance marble floors when holidaying abroad. When it is so hot outside most people would not think for a second that cool floors is not good for their little, growing bladder and kidneys. It is not for adults either though.

If it is fashionable to wear something exposing your midriff or your kidney area, your lower back area for goodness sake please do not follow the fashion, if the weather is cold. Getting damp, cold or draughts (Giraffes as I call them) into your body is seriously bad for your health. Young women who get repeatedly cold or damp are going to be making their monthly cycles far worse and often more painful, or may also start having problems when it comes to conception. What egg wants to be fertilized in a freezing and damp environments?.

Equally guys the quality of your sperm will be affected also by how cold you have allowed your kidneys and bladder energy lines to become.

So the fashion of younger men to wear trousers that jam up their hips and make them walk like penguins are producing two health hazards at once. Structurally they are seriously messing up their hip, pelvis and back with being so constrained by belts slung at totally the wrong angle for their bodies. They then are causing so much heat from the friction of the movement of their own legs being jammed too close together which will affect the sperm count, and the natural flow of energy. Information is key.

Men but more likely women stop wearing too tight jeans or anything that actually crushes and scrunches up the area between your legs. As again you are creating heat which your body will then try to get rid of by you having bladder issues.

Women be seriously aware of what dyes you are putting on your hair. It will be absorbed by your body and your kidneys take a massive hit so your water, your bladder too is being polluted. Thank God it is now fashionable to be white or grey, and I also totally get that you still will want to use dyes so please just spend more money and do your homework about what you are putting on your hair. Do not pay the price later on with a polluted water system that cannot cope. What you put on your hair does come through your own filter system so be wise about what you are asking of your body when you use dyes.

118

Have checked properly by a qualified nutritionist your vitamin and mineral status if you are discovering that you are incredibly anxious all of the time. Always start with the physical first and eliminate if your anxiety is not coming from a mineral or vitamin deficiency which now is sadly very possible and getting more so. Go to someone who knows what they are doing, has a good reputation and does not hook you into years of taking supplements that also your body might not be digesting or absorbing. Your body often just needs a little help and not necessarily long term. Do not go to someone who wants to bully you on any level about your health. There are plenty of great and integrated people out there but you need to be persistent and tenacious to find one, use your water element to find one. Be clever and wise.

If you are discovering that you are really operating with huge amounts of anxiety then become willing to seek proper help. Learning to breathe properly will make a huge difference but not from someone who has not got a clue as there may be a damn good reason why you are still holding your breath. If so have enough self-respect, self-care and love to be wise, seek medical advice to ensure there is not any underlying medical issue. If not then seek a therapist, or a person who is qualified to help you unlock what is stuck in you and needs releasing.

If you know that you are damaging your relationships with how controlling you are, or how dishonest you have the habit of being, seek some help to unravel the whys. That way you can find some peace with those aspects of yourself that are indicating loudly that you need support.

Acupuncture of course can and does release all sorts of things but I am not writing a book to sell a particular mode of treatment. Unravel dis-ease Naturally is to empower you to start finding your own way. To find ways with what might be needed to move your life force and energy on when and if it is getting stuck, for a host of usually very good reasons. It is great if you begin to understand how miraculous your own body and its systems are. So set about finding what model of treatment or help might help you deal with your anxiety. Trust your gut instinct. Preferably find someone who sees what is right with you and does not treat you with all that they may clearly perceive is wrong with you. Which will only happen if they are treating you through the filter of being so focused on what is wrong with themselves! That is already unhelpful and will not allow you to feel safe. You must take responsibility for feeling safe. If at any point you do not feel safe with a practitioner do NOT give your power away to them. However qualified, they are human and need to be respectful of your journey. There is a very common tendency to get caught up in a very anxious making frenzy when confronted with the idea that perhaps you are resistant to your own wellbeing or you are sabotaging. In my own experience with patients and their energy it is vital to encourage them to hear their own opinion and judgements, instincts. They know their own bodies far better than any of us practitioners. Do NOT let someone else assess why and what you are up to when you simply may feel unsafe. Unsafe for very good reasons. Being fragile and vulnerable with anyone else who has knowledge that you do not have has to be taken into account. If the consultant, practitioner that you are seeing, in other words is not being humble and helpful with their knowledge it is likely that you will not feel safe. If you then express that something is not working for you it is never a coincidence that you will then be intimidated, bullied or told that you are just in "resistance" to their greater understanding of your situation. If you get a whiff of such arrogance run for the hills! Trust yourself. It is your life so when you are ready to deal with something you actually will, despite others imposing on you some of their ideas of when or how you deal with your own stuck energy. There are far too many practitioners on all sorts of levels who are not safe to unravel your knots with or how stuck you might be.

So please step by step deal with your anxiety, as it is talking to you and will get louder if you do not listen to it. Keep looking until you find the right person. I cannot stress this enough. Equally if you are now beginning to realize that you live with a total disregard for yours or others safety and find danger a huge turn on you may want to go directly to your nearest and best Integrated Chinese Medical Practitioner and have them begin to put you back in balance. For your sake and others.

On the subject of listening and then hearing start with serious intent clocking whether you are a good listener and then also hearing others. Do you start a conversation and then talk immediately babbling on without really giving the other person a chance. Are you a bore with your lack of ability to listen. Are you careless with your lack of listening or hearing skills?

Often patients would ask me what was the single most important thing that they could learn to improve their relationships.

My answer was always the same. Learn to listen and to really hear without having to fix, identify or speak yourself. First though you have to listen to yourself I would always add.

Pay attention to yourself, stop being careless with your own precious bladder. Lastly when you want to have a pee please go do not keep holding on.

Discovering and Listening to your body is the best way to treasure yourself and then others.

Summary of the Bladder chapter

Bladder

The Bladder is associated with the Winter Season

The element is water

The colour is blue

The sound is groaning

The odour is putrid

The emotion/energy is fear/anxiety

The function of this organ is to be responsible for the storage of fluid and its elimination.

The associated organ is Kidney (Chapter 3)

A balanced Winter provides the ability to :

- Notice danger, assessing the extent of risk being presented

- Take action to deal with risks in appropriate ways

- Provide reassurance about safety.

Behaviours that can become evident when the Winter is out of balance within us. These are the extremes that we may sense in ourselves or others.

Intimidating	to	reassuring
Driven	to	no drive
Taking risks	to	being over cautious/ imagining the worst
Distrusting	to	overly trusting

Chapter 5

Discover your

Gallbladder

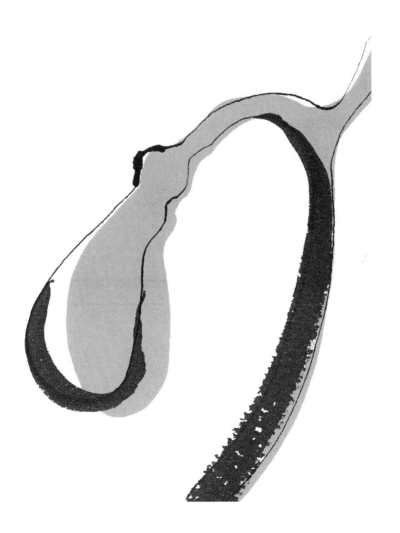

Beyond A Place Where There Is No Hope - Gallbladder

The season is spring, the colour green and the nature is Wind, with the emotion being anger.

The word anger is used to convey almost totally the opposite of how it is thought of generally. The Gallbladder is called the decision maker. It is said that the interaction between our liver and gallbladder energy empower an integrated seeing (vision) of our inner and outer worlds. The gallbladder literally conveys the vision of the liver to the outside world, overseeing discernment with determination stemming from the functions of it.. Each and every organ has a different form of depression that stems from the organ energy not functioning properly. When the organs of both the liver and gallbladder are out of balance it is possible that a patient will say that they are depressed, with no sense of horizon or future. They will often refer to there being no hope. Their vision for any future is gone. They are looking out into the world, only experiencing blankness due to the extreme of the energy getting stuck or stagnant.

My father taught me how to live elegantly with an ongoing, relentless level of suffering that he had himself with a mistake made at his birth. One moment perfect and the next, a mistake made by a midwife, left one side of him paralysed. His cars, shoes and clothes all were adapted for his "gammy side "as he affectionately called it.

In an age when we whitewash, sometimes ignore or even spiritually spin, the levels of suffering that are in this world he cleverly taught me to live alongside pain. Transforming all forms of suffering when possible for yourself or others. Even to, at times, wear it lightly, having the courage and audacity to disarm it, almost like a favourite jacket that you throw proudly over your shoulders. Proudly as it brings so much with it, that is not at first visible. With time, like the great leather of the jacket, its weathering makes it appear even lovelier. I do not intend to glamorise suffering though. The point of this chapter is to share the harshness of seasonal weather being a part of our lives and not something that we endlessly try to sanitise, which not only does not serve us, but it hinders what we are really needing to be and do.

Where is the hope when you receive a hammer blow of a prognosis, or a sudden realisation from a will that you are not only left with nothing, and you have huge debts to pay off.? Where are you to find justice? Debts left by an adored husband that had you totally believing that your lifestyle was manageable for him? You are devastated beyond any sort of place that you can imagine ever finding any hope again. All you see before you is dying wretchedly with no control of any aspect of your body, let alone mind. You remember something that is like a horror story in the filing of your mind that has come to the forefront about how you can drown in your own fluids, with this particular prognosis. OR you are going to be destitute, just like the woman you pitied only yesterday giving her a tenner, before rushing off wondering how she managed. The following two stories are examples of the Spring and Wood energy being out of balance.

In the first examples case the patient's husband was a bit of a bully, although fundamentally it was a good and happy relationship from his wife's perspective, as long as she did not get involved at all in their finances which he considered to be an insult to his manhood. She genuinely had no idea what a mess he was making of their lives, pensions and all other financial arrangements, until the "appalling day when our solicitor read me the will and explained in terrifying minute detail the reality of the mess I was left with".

She was very timid and sighed a lot when arriving in the clinic. Each sigh came with a heavy sense of total hopelessness. She often would wake in the night and then not be able to get back to sleep for hours and was restless when she did sleep. When I asked her if she felt any anger towards her husband she nervously replied "No, no not at all, poor Bunny, he must have felt so alone having refused to let me help him. It's so sad as I am good at figures. What a mess, what a terrible mess, there is no hope, none at all".

Again, the expression of our life force towards what we individually need to be, to create, to do is necessary for our health. Energy unexpressed sooner or later becomes like a block in our guttering systems. The stagnant energy lies dormant seemingly, but actually turning to what we call wind as the frustrations turn to blocked anger, then to rage, we can then become gale force winds internally that will blow sooner or later, in some form. The dynamic expression within us needs to be given direction. If unexpressed, as in the case of this patient, she just became more nervous and timid. It was her timidity that allowed the step son to get the idea that he would be able to ride roughshod over her, when the Will was read, ignoring his father's wishes .

The energy becomes weakened, or we can describe it as empty. Having been left the estate as the sole beneficiary she had total power over and above a step son that was attempting to rob her of what could be salvaged. She realised that he had been trying to put his own debts under his father's umbrella, so with some treatments and support of her Gallbladder energy she began to come out of herself. The ways that she had surpassed her own life force to be happy in her marriage suddenly were coming out. It was her, not the accountants, lawyers or any of the other parties involved to `help her',who found solutions.

Within 5 years of very hard work she not only prevented bankruptcy, but was able to salvage the farm, diversifying in a way that meant the estate became very profitable, which she thrived on. Not only that, but her timidity had disappeared, her nerves were as steady as a rock and she ended up having a reputation amongst the other farmers as being like a poker player and very steely but fair, so no one could or would dare take advantage of this seemingly elderly woman. It amused her a lot how much she had changed but her remark one day to me was a very telling one.

"Of course I love being who I am now but Bunny was not secure enough to have liked these aspects of me at all. Our marriage would never have lasted. Funny that really, when I first saw you I so believed that I had reached a point beyond hope and yet now really I am much more financially secure for real than we ever were, even at the height of Bunny's pretence's. I was too timid and too frightened to get involved and perhaps really deep down I knew how insecure he was, so I suppose really I chose to keep being the timid, nervous one in our relationship so that he could and would appear to shine."

The following is another example of what we call "wood energy misfiring".

Writing this I find myself again having another spell in hospital. It never seems a so called coincidence to me when examples of what I am thinking about arrives. So through a blur of incredibly strong pain relief I was amused when a consultant walked in yesterday who was so green around his face, in all the areas that suggest to a practitioner that his Wood, spring energy is being blocked. He was so bullying and arrogant in his attitude that I deliberately engaged him in conversation about himself which usually works as a 'pattern interrupt'. In other words it usually has the effect of getting certain types of medics out of their pompous stances, where inevitably at your lowest you will be treated as just 'another case', rather than a fellow human being. He actually told me how he was bored in other areas of his chosen and original aspect of medicine. From one question I was able to diagnose one of his underlying and crucial life force issues, that was begging to be listened to. However it became clear by how he was with me, that he was as far away as you could get from connecting to himself, let alone his patients. He was totally unaware of his behaviour or his words. He has a reputation for arrogance, for looking through and below all the nurses, but is considered brilliant at his job. It is simply not possible for a person to be as good as their potential is actually designed for when their energy is blocked. I refused to see him again and deliberately made my feelings known about this unacceptable arrogance. Sheepishly, at the end of a long and horrible ten days he arrived, clearly shaken from his no doubt uncomfortable perch, and was reduced to a kindness that initially was deeply unsettling for him. Without him knowing it I had treated his wood energy so he left smiling and engaged. Unfortunately Gallbladder and liver energy gone off balance can come across as bullying, arrogance, staccato voices that defy anyone to question what appears to be their authority. By calling him through essentially well primed gossip on his attitude I had deliberately challenged his boredom, borne out of mostly patients and fellow colleagues being on the one hand in awe of his brilliance and on the other resentful of this high handiness. Neither of these fed his need for interactions that would fuel his sense of unique purpose, or aid his humanity that was floundering with what to do with his brilliance.

The Gallbladder is also associated with the Wood, so as in the Spring, everything blooms. We too can access, and harness that extraordinarily internal and natural capacity. We have the capacity to literally have a spring in our step, to spring forth after

128

the winter where it appears as if we are doing nothing while we are hibernating, as if we will not ever be able to resurrect from the darkness and silence of the previous season, the shorter days where it has seemed as if the world of nature has died. Yet in the Spring our bodies are propelling us into decisions, like seeds deeply in the ground that will one day become a glorious tree. We and they need to go through the processes and timings involved in becoming what their destiny has within them. Literally like a of packet seeds, stacked in shelves at the garden centres its almost inconceivable that a static seed can, within a season, become a flower, vegetable or plant with some outside help. Just put that seed in the ground and even if you forget it so often it just does the rest and fights its way through the resistance of all that surrounds it to spring out of the earth.

You too can help each and every one of your amazing organs. In every season you can become more familiar with all aspects of yourself, in an integrated and interconnected way.

If however the traumas of the past are not released properly and safely they will find a way out somehow and in some form. Where there is a recurring sense of life beyond hope is exactly how and sometimes where our bodies will spit out any unresolved trauma. For instance it is never ever a coincidence when a patient diagnosed with cancer, or another terrifying dis-ease, is able to understand the beginnings of where their own energy systems were overloaded by events. During an extensive integrated diagnosis, that is the time for the patient to identify almost exactly the moment when all sorts of situations happened that were just too shocking or too much to be dealt with. The next time you are quick to condemn a symptom or a state of dis-ease see if you can first make sure that there isn't a bigger subtext that needs releasing, witnessing and healing. We all have layers to release. 'The sins of the forefathers' is energetically what so often Integrated Practitioners are looking at. Ignorance and arrogance mixed with the heady and continual vapour of fear is handed down from one generation to the next, when the laws of nature are ignored. Raging through families, for an example, can become a way of life, an acceptable norm which it certainly is not to your body. Rage is incredibly dangerous if you do not learn how to steer, harness and not be controlled by it.

So for instance, as another personal example, I found myself feeling wretched and bizarrely guilty after the five last surgeries. Being a practitioner is a two edged sword as often people can make remarks like "why can't you heal yourself?" or "but doesn't your form of medicine work then?", if they discover that you are not well. It is the marriage of two systems that have kept me alive over and over again, against so many odds, so as I was facing more of how out of control I was increasingly, so I too began experiencing facing a life beyond hope. I was overly exposed, seemingly, to the world of no one actually understanding how to really help on most levels, with the three main conditions that I have. It was so shocking to be in such isolation, and to somehow not have any influence over the utter devastation that my life seemed to represent. Whilst on heavy pain killing drugs my liver and gallbladder were being affected, so I struggled with what I knew was also partly a chemical depression. That mixed with nothing being familiar or representing anything that I had already worked so hard to obtain left me with a weird sense of having failed myself, and at a time when I needed my own support the most. This in turn actually became a gift as it released more of the neglect of my childhood. It was the combination of the visceral memories of the past, along with the lack of care in the immediate present time that was too much for me. Hence it was the integrated feedback mechanism within me that was cleverly forcing another layer of unresolved frustration out of my being. It has only been within the framework of what this book is about that I now live with access to my own dynamic life force and energy again. Except of course when I don't and land in a puddle of hopelessness!. To then find it again, and again. Season after season. The total sense of hopelessness turned into the treasured experience of discovering more how really amazing we are.

I become with each passing year so, amazed at exactly what my mother and grandmother had to cope with, in living also with these genetic challenges. I understand why they increasingly self-medicated the pains, fears and horrors of being so isolated with such a rare condition.

Over time I have begun to understand that actually our bodies are constantly propelling us to a greater vision - an automatic sense of drive and purpose. Each and every time I have another roadblock put in front of me personally, or another part of me will not physically work in the way that I want I find myself diverting, driven to find another way. I keep asserting myself in ways that I would have said was not possible. In so many ways now and on so many levels there is no hope for life, as I so wanted it to be. The decisions I need to make in a day are mostly around how to structure and order the increasing demands of this medical challenge, that literally requires all of my attention and then some, whilst also being continually mindful of having as thriving a life as possible. The decision making of when to ignore a blinding migraine in my teeth and jaw, to an eyeball suddenly feeling as if there is so much pressure behind it that I become sure it will just pop out of its socket or what to do when a ruptured disc means I just can not move. Or the lovely Pilates teacher who is helping me try to get some fitness back takes one look at me and goes "NO, we are not doing anything with you today". On those occasions she is the boundary I need, as I can get so frustrated at the constant restraints on my life that I want to burst and push way beyond my capacity. Which will result in more agony.

All of the boundaries, structure, planning is to do with the wood element. My days become an experience of how much more we can become. Our spring energy can allow for a gentle acceptance of even the most ruthless of times. We can become so strengthened through the painful cutting back of seemingly everything.

I have always insisted that I stop all drugs as soon as is possible after these surgeries as I know that my liver and gallbladder energy needs to be as clear as possible for me to be able to keep making sane, rational, energetically sound decisions around my endless layers of recovering.

Having had three separate cancer diagnosis I have to be the one amongst everyone who insists, after for instance coughing for too long, that my lungs are checked. To be super vigilant is necessary, vital even whilst also making sure to thrive beside this all. Layer by layer I have to become the best friend that I can be to myself first and foremost, to have the eyes (vision) of hope and kindness towards a new season and future, even in the absence of being able yet to 'see' it.

If you look out at nature and the Spring energy a seedling will find its way out from seemingly impossible restraints. I have seen tree roots find ways into houses. It is as if the house would prevent that seed from growing, being propelled out, forward and through. YET when the time is right inside that spring energy it has to emerge and start its path of growth, even through concrete or whatever is blocking its path. We too are like that, our frustrations are literally the spring energy emerging and needing, wanting to express itself. By learning to befriend the layers of frustrations that we all will and do have we can discover more of what we or others are to.

Again and again where there honestly seems no hope of growth or expansion then we can and do gain a profound sense of what I call the subtext that is to be found in all of life. (Amongst many gifts that get ignited is often humour with the spring energy). As the sap rises literally everything becomes a little frisky, mischievous and expansive. As our own energy seems to become richer and deeper often not taking anything too seriously, except when of course we do, and land in a heap of momentarily thinking, feeling an intense seriousness about everything. So before the Spring energy can burst through with our plans, the energy to assert and direct the cold dark hibernating winter has to be gone through. Where we have gathered our resources to literally spring forth.

When our Wood energy though is stuck and stagnant we can be so apathetic on one hand whilst rigid, defiant, even seeking justice for situations that essentially are not appropriate for us to deal with, for what our real resources require.

A runner came to me as his tendons were bothering him a lot. Tendons are very much connected to the gallbladder. He was totally inflexible and rigid about his running and would not cut back on his schedules. He was furious about the injustice in a political situation in another country but when I discussed his own son being bullied he was apathetic that it was happening. He had dropped it into the conversation and was even suggesting that it would be good for his son as he too was bullied. His tone in his voice though would drop when discussing it. I asked him about the bullying that he had received. He became almost shifty and wrapped his arms firmly around his body and could not look at me. Later during treatment he began to talk. It became clear that he had been badly shamed, humiliated and verbally bullied over many years by even the teachers. He was picked on because he was incredibly intelligent and always ahead of everyone else. However instead of being praised or encouraged for being so clever he was isolated. He hadn't realised until treatments began that he had hated being so clever and in fact was seeking justice in places that were not his direct responsibility because he felt so powerless over direct situations .At one point a moment of revelation dawned on him, his tone of voice became strong and assertive, crystal clear

"I must do something about my son, like me he is very clever and I am simply ignoring the problem. Of course I can do something about it now. I am the adult. I will stop spending so much energy and time away from my family. I get it; I have been misdirecting my time and energy. "

"I have been literally activating my own tendons in the wrong way haven't I?" He chuckled to himself leaving the question hanging in the air.

"I never knew that this was all so connected, I am even feeling less rigid about my training. Has that been damaging me? Was I in fact running from all of that bottled up and unresolved stuff from my past?"

I had explained to him how our Wood energy can give us a huge sense of compassion and benevolence towards the world but so too it can easily be misdirected.

For instance a wealthy benefactor will share his land with neglected animals from zoos shutting down or just with no home but will forget continually to feed his own dog regularly. Or a lawyer will walk in with an arrogant swagger treating clients and the admin staff as if they are all idiots and yet can tend to his orchids as if they were clients that needed so much care and attention. He remains oblivious to how obnoxious his behaviour is and in fact no one else really notices how green he is literally all over his face, flashing out like a beacon to anyone qualified to see or hear how distressed his Gall Bladder is. Insidiously he begins to not be able to tolerate cream, cheeses or fatty foods. He is stretched and irritable in all areas except with his orchids who don't answer back at him. Even his wife knows not to come out to disturb him when he tending to them. She swallows her resentment and feels so sad and lonely whilst giving herself a hard time for being envious of orchids, hating it when a friend gives her another one.

So each and every decision we make is going in a direction that we are steering or is being steered for us. Even inwardly we can make decisions if it is not possible outwardly. No one of us will escape moments or times in our lives where it seems as if we have no choices outwardly. Or as if all we are coming up against is such resistance we want to give up. One of the amazing practitioners that has treated me for years broke her back and was told that she would never walk again. Having trained in Qi Gong for years, before the accident, she practiced it in her head whilst unable to move until her body began to move again.

It becomes so extraordinarily comforting for instance knowing that there are endless references whether they be religious, philosophical or as in Chinese Medicine to all of life being a perpetual movement through levels of resistance. There is nothing personal about it.

This is what the Wood energy is all about. The bamboo for instance that is hollow can bend almost completely backwards so that when the winds come it can be detached, empty and bend with the winds. Interestingly if it was full of "matter" it would not have the flexibility needed to do the bending that is needed every which way according to the way the winds are moving. This is such a metaphor for our own lives. Real peaceful living is attained by really practising being empty i.e. being detached from all that we are in fact taught to be so attached to.

Have you ever noticed that when you can still your own noise of your own being; when in front of another person, and just 'be' with, beside and for that person, empty of you; available for them that something totally amazing always happen?. A real connection takes place, rather than the two of you both walking away slightly frustrated without really registering that you are. Rather like walking away from a meal and yet still feeling hungry. Endlessly there are paradoxes, seeming contradictions as only when you begin to know yourself step by step can you even begin to grasp how to then stand aside, being available for another, actually wanting to.

In other chapters I will be talking about connections, communications, however in this chapter it is your decision maker, the gallbladder that facilitates, from minute to minute, deeper and more benevolent and enhancing directions to be taking place in life. Decision making actually makes or breaks our days, opportunities and the directions for our lives in every possible way.

Going back to my own father's example, 21 consultants had told his mother, my grandmother that her son would never walk. She simply refused to believe it so she kept going until one consultant said "If you are prepared to make your son do painful exercises for the first few years of his life then he will learn to walk". It is no wonder then, that by the time he became a father, to two children that he never thought that he could or would have, he was wearing his dignity mixed with a sage humour like an old well-worn leather jacket and proudly so. It had taken him years of every possible resistance, blocks, bullying, humiliations and isolations to find his path. He and his mother had balanced Gall bladder energy that lead to decisions, which kept creating a way forward despite and with every single block. They just incorporated all resistance into their decisions. A mother's decision to decide that her child would walk, with then my own father's determination to succeed with his decision making in every area that he could.

As some aspects of our daily living is taken away from the seasons and nature's rhythms, perhaps we lose touch with the endless gentle and subliminal reminders of how much everything in life is a process. The actual rhythms can be soothing reminders of the revelations yet to come. As we master being closer to what the greatest truths have always been we can be at times proud of understanding the next layer. We can celebrate getting the next joke, the next subtext, we can smile joyfully, no longer resisting life, as we see the purposes of the endless changes, so suddenly they are holding no power over us. In fact we are grateful, humbled by experiencing being just part of the soup of humanity together. Our awakening to the changing perspectives reveals the next bit of the puzzle for us. What once seemed unfathomable, even untenable suddenly can seem as if it's the most normal of realities that you enjoy embodying. That there is indeed a place to go with our realities, we don't have to ignore, fix or deny what is, by firstly doing the opposite e.g. acknowledging where ever we are at we can then be transformed to the next level.

Popular culture emphasises the training of the mind as being the way to master our lives, not fully appreciating that the mind is in all of our cells. Our mind is not separate from the rest of our bodies. As we can influence our bodies with our thoughts, our bodies influence the way we think. In our working through our own discomforts, dis-ease, senses of doubts or guilt we do not fully take on board our own subtle influence, or the lens with which we are looking through all of life, is having on what we see or experience. We so often do carry vague senses of guilts that have been carried through the generations but continue to influence our behaviours and choices, without us realising fully what is happening. At this point it is so easy to be seduced by other's perspectives, when we are not yet fully aware of why or how we even believe something or someone. This too is just another layer of what I call traction or initiation that we all will go and grow through. Our perspective is something that does indeed need to be constantly challenged so that our sometimes firmly held belief systems can be reviewed.

There are systems of medicine being used in the world that are known to align themselves totally with Nature, 5000 years' worth of practical evidence, contrary to the other modern medicine which is 100 to 150 years old. There is in our DNA the integrated truth constantly propelling us to the freedom of the truth. Teachings throughout this existence are all saying the same things. Some teach a one dimensional perspective though that keeps us doused in a treacle of confusion and shame, whilst others, (generally not so easy to find and slightly hidden) are just quietly freeing us.

There exists so many references, clues and traditional teachings to show us how to go back home to where the suffering, that we all do have and go through, leads us back to peace. Home is the place inside us that we can become increasingly settled with, accepting of what we have to accept and equally of what we can change. I am not so sure now in my own understanding of today that the peace is a stable static continuum; it makes no sense to me. All of life is constant change so peace too is a moving energy that gets richer for accessing what has gone before us, harnessing the collective consciousness. My definition of peace now is mastering the energy of my daily reality, not resisting the normal moving process (except of course when I do).

We are living the midst of a world that promotes almost insidiously the illusion that all suffering can be eradicated, sorted or fixed. The new adverts most recently promoting some pain killer proudly captions, "We don't let pain dictate to us ". In other words do not graciously stop and listen to the profound wisdom the greatest friend (your body) will ever have is telling you. Actually guiding you deeper into the wonderment of your own individual path and skills, even your purpose this lifetime.

At all costs we are taught to systematically dismiss, ignore any hint of in fact never ever being in control of ourselves   We just continue to live with the rather delicious, at times, illusion of our seeming abilities to control ourselves, others and our lives. Rather than living alongside nature, within us and entirely integrated with all aspects of life.

They say in all of the twelve step programmes (self-help meetings to help people chart their ways through addictions of all sorts and, or living with people suffering from addictions):-

"If you want to give God a laugh, tell him your plans".

While I am on the incredibly badly marketed subject of God, no, I do not think some cruel universal master taunts us or sends these appalling situations that so many have to go through. Although of course at times we will project all sorts of our weird and wacky perspectives on to our ideas of a God or perhaps worse still our taught notions of God. Although as our sense of our selves develops which is hugely a part of the Spring and Wood energy, our connection to our own maturity, spirituality and sexuality grow. They are totally entwined as we slowly begin to grasp, hopefully by the time you have finished reading both chapters on your own Wood energy.

As we develop and drop so many perspectives that do not stand up to the test of time or our own individual experiences we are no longer still taken in by the cons as they are so pervasive in our generalised western cultures. Religions of the past were insidiously used to controlling the masses by a chosen few and now too, modern so-called spiritual self-help is doing the same. Both can ignite a sense of guilt and misery. Even overwhelm, with a heightened sense of inadequacy before we have even begun the inner journeys of literal self-discovery. So, as a general rule of thumb, real spiritual wisdom actually does the opposite of shaming and binding us. However challenging, it actually immediately has the capacity to sooth and ignite in us a sense of oneness, of our innocence (not our guilt).

Having to have massive lifesaving and changing surgeries twice in the middle of my training as an integrated Chinese medical practitioner I became initially much more trained than I had originally planned. Of course at the time I wailed inwardly, thinking it was more proof of my failure as a human being as I was not going to finish with my friends. I, of course, forgot totally at the time that I had only gone into the training as I was the step mother of two beautiful children, too ill to work full time. So wanting to be qualified in something that would allow me to be at home working on days that I was well enough. I abandoned myself with forgetting totally vital information so then was very unkind in my irrational emotional response to the results. My rational at the time was that if anything was to happen to the children's father, when their mother was already suffering deeply and fighting for her own sense of wellbeing I would be able to provide for their future. My sense of guilt and misery at not ever being able to go through a day without a host of disconnected, seemingly, signs and symptoms arising, was deeply imbedded, though.

The ways in which the college marked me and refused to let me go further, to then stop me from sitting the written exams, fed into my sense of rejection and utter failure. As I had got 74.5 % twice with point location exams that needed 75% to pass it was so tantalisingly close. On both occasions, unwisely, I stubbornly went to do the exams after having epileptic type, but conscious, seizures during the nights before the exams. Little did any of us fully understand that with enormous bone spurs growing into my spine that, in the wrong positions for too long, the results were terrifying fits. Revising hunched over the books was the trigger physically. I would know that I was going to lose full control of my own body then fighting for my breath whilst my body flayed around uncontrollably. So in hindsight either I could have been given some leeway with the exam as I was clearly ill or I could have waited. It was one of the harshest moments of my life reading the results. To be so far and yet to immediately know that the rules would not allow me to go further just fed into my shattered but building self-esteem.

Eighteen people who I did not even know very well heard about the results and attempted to get the college to reconsider the decision so I will forever remember their passionate fury at the injustice. If I had been able to surrender too and accept my reality I would have remembered how ill I was and immediately given myself some slack, perhaps even being amazed at how far I had come. As my training stretched to 9 years from three the TAO (the way), which is the foundation of Integrated medicine, became so deeply familiar to me that I now am profoundly grateful.

We were endlessly shown how we only thought we could see, smell, hear, know and feel. Endlessly we were shown ways of developing our skills. Both wrists for instance have six pulses with each one having 28 individual rhythms which can give us, the more we practise, very accurate information on each and every function as well as organ in the body. Nothing is disconnected so it becomes impossible to not to begin automatically to master one's own being.

The balance that is possible in all circumstances becomes the norm rather than a random hit and miss event.

It is interesting that there is a marriage beginning to take place between the East and the West medically (and incorporating quantum physics and the sciences alongside metaphysics). Which will of course provide more of the answers that are out there, and have always been. Although they are only beginning to be available now to the masses with the great aspects of what the internet can and does provide.

The world to a huge extent still ignores, denies and insidiously punishes suffering so with more knowledge it does become easier, when possible, to counter some of the punishing with knowledge. Stopping the manipulations as well, whilst in the throes of suffering, which of course only goes to make the suffering worse when it's happening. It is the double whammy that seems so often to come, or even the treble whammy, or any amount of numbers.

Knowledge of our own individual and unique beings begins to mean that we get to negotiate the initiations that we will all go through at some point. Whatever your perspective or level of consciousness there is in all ways going to be the shifts that propel us all into continuing evolution of our souls/spirits, our own unique path. Life is a continual kaleidoscope of differing points of view, initially in discord and then eventually sounding as one. Interestingly if a room full of people are left to find their oneness through sound very quickly they actually harmonise together. So too with truth setting us free. There is often literally a physical sensation of a Yes that is so profound it bats out any of our other previously "convinced" yes's!! A wilful forced Yes is so different to our wholehearted yes from our bellies. Wood energy is very much the energy that gives you the capacity to find your own unique path, when in balance it is about developing yourself.

We will all eventually master our emotional, physical and spiritual aspects by going home to the inner harmony that is without effort where the harshness of language in so many ways is left behind. The true frequencies of love need no speaking language. As behaviour and actions speak louder, so too does the functioning of our integrated beings.

As our Gallbladder is our decision maker there will be many times in our lives when we will be brought consciously or even unconsciously to places of surrender – acceptance to something far greater than at times our limited imaging's.

I surrendered on the day of my engagement to the enforced reality of lying in a hospital waiting to see if my body would naturally abort the second of two babies. I had had a twin ectopic pregnancy, but having brought me around from the laser surgery they had only been able to deal with one of the pregnancies. I surrendered but I was not able to fully accept it until years had passed and the full extent of my diagnosis became clearer. I was only able to accept and integrate the full wisdom of that clever twist of fate when it was clear my babies would also have had the diseases that my grandmother, mother and I carry. It was very tough but a relief not to impose what I struggle with on to what would have been our children. Meanwhile that surgery triggered me into even worse full-blown fits eventually showing a brilliant surgeon that I had bone growths growing into the spinal column. He had no idea why I was able to walk at all.

Again and again, so far in my life, as medical chaos has reigned bringing about a continual heart-breaking series of consequences I have been faced with realising that I don't have the full facts ever. Nothing is as it seems. Ultimately my life and the power to keep walking was saved by the two little souls daring to be conceived in a body that they would have known couldn't have carried them. It was a big job they did, perhaps that's why they came in together and then completed the assignment of saving my life by going out separately. Literally between the first leaving my body, in the sense of the blood work and the second my future had changed.

Coming from a very confusing and unhappy childhood that had begun with seven long years of being almost totally deaf I had built a fantasy to tease myself through the hell. In my fantasy the day my engagement was announced was the day my childhood nightmares would be over, I had told myself and worked towards for years. No one had noticed or had the time to respond to my deafness with any other than, how naughty and defiant I was. If you are deaf and no one notices, it gives you an extraordinary experience of being blind as well, simply because others blindness becomes a projection that then has you feeling mad as well. Not a great combination!

My darling mother was in such extreme difficulties herself that she quickly became convinced that I was a difficult, demanding, attention seeking, dim-witted hypochondriac. She also never believed a word I said so very quickly I became convinced that my own sense of truth and my instinct was wrong and very faulty.

So the announcement day of my engagement wasn't anywhere near my imagined and well-rehearsed picture.

In fact it could not have been more different.

How was my own gallbladder going to cope?

My beloved and very frightened mother arrived drunk and broken by the weight of her life. I remember looking at her and my fiancé, knowing that I was being propelled into another layer of an unknown that was very different from my fantasy.

My own mother's gallbladder energy was constantly being overburdened with her choices. Unknown to her she was ever increasingly self-medicating the very disease that I have. NO amount of sedating her pains and struggles was going to stop the demons within her, mostly the worst, it seems, being her self-hatred. Her continual loss of control with herself would have propelled her into more isolation and self-loathing, which in turn will have been passed on to her by her mother. They both came from generations that lived the beliefs that you suffered in silence and certainly under no circumstances did you explore possibilities of sharing your experience. Labelling of 'hysteria', female issues, mad, etc. etc. would have been hauntingly bandied about whilst she was at the worst and most fragile times of her own life.

No one had the depth of knowledge to free my mother or grandmother during their lifetimes.

She was extraordinarily brave, though unable to be the mother she would have wanted to be to me, she made many other people's lives slightly easier with her huge humour, daring and outrageous style.

I once asked why on earth she was cartwheeling down Beecham Place, a stylish street in the heart of London, of course being very young I didn't know whether to be appalled and embarrassed or really rather proud of my hippy mother.

"For fun darling, Why?"

When she had made up her mind to die and wanted nothing else, she was hugely disappointed when it didn't look as if she would get her wish for a very short time in the mess of her diagnosis and prognosis. The cancer therapist was sent in, and by some amazing good fortune I was in my mother's hospital room. I witnessed this rather typical affect my mother had on others. Clearly thrown by the titles my mother had accumulated towards the end of her life she plumped for a mumbled

"Your ladyship", which my mother clearly adored and even tried to sit up taller for. "How do you feel about your, the diagnosis?" Was spluttered out.

The still very clear and very blue eyes shot this poor brave woman a glance that I am not sure she will ever forget.

I will not, "Feel, well,.............. I have never had this before, so it's really rather exciting, why, how do you feel?"

The therapist was totally thrown, but to her credit I could see her almost whizzing through all her training to see if in this bizarre unexpected response there was any help to be had.

"Precisely yes I see, well, but the prognosis how do you feel about that?"

Mummy smiled with a delicious smile briefly as if all was well with her world.

"That's the beauty of this situation, you see I have never died before so that is the bit I am particularly looking forward to" with which the eyes dismissed the startled woman.

My mother took charge of her dying, as she had lived in a place beyond hope, I suspect for many years. There by she gave it hope and died partying in her way and on her terms, demanding no pity be within miles of her. She finally understood that she was loved, she was safe and that it was more than ok for her to go home to somewhere that she passionately believed she would be free in.

Unglamorous Tips For Glamorous Living
Or Tantalising Tips

Just watch for even half a day how many decisions you are making.

Watch for your own interest and learning how your decision making goes 'south':

- when you are tired,

- have been working on a computer for too long

- have become overloaded emotionally.

- Not done enough stimulating activities or movement.

Appreciate for even a short while how this organ helps you decide which yogurt to have, which type of relationship, all of your yes or no answers to anything.

Decide to learn the difference between your NO (it is vital that you know that it is a full sentence) and your resistance to something that, for your own growth and wellbeing you must go through. Most of my patients were easily intimidated by not knowing the difference. I certainly did not, so it became one of the most valuable tools medically when I WAS able to clearly distinguish between the two.

Just think for one moment what it would be like if you had no capacity to make decisions. Be kind and generous when you come across those people amongst us who seem incapable of making decisions. Bother to find out what is happening as often they need help unravelling what and why they have lost the natural capacity to make decisions. Bullying is so rife in our society that for some a timidity becomes their normal way of conducting themselves. So for your own boomeranging sake deliberately decide to SEE if there is some way you can facilitate, at the very least, some kindness. It will make the timid person less anxious and may well be a part of them finding their own gallbladder energy.

Even when your gallbladder is removed the energetic pattering that has an influence beyond the actual organ allowed for decision making is still taking place.

If your gall bladder seems to be giving you problems please before you have it removed go to great lengths to educate yourself about what in fact your gallbladder is saying. With the editors wise advice I took out a harrowing story about a patient who ended up keeping her gall bladder, but not before seriously uncovering what was really going on. Removing the gallbladder does not necessarily deal with the real issues. This is an enormous subject alone but well worth you doing your own research, on a mind, body and spirit level.

Find someone who is familiar with the Vagus nerve if your gallbladder is having problems. Forgive me please for this being really tantalizing. Hopefully perhaps enough so to have you do your homework.

Integrated practitioners are doing superb work with every type of problems, so be willing to find the right one for you if your gallbladder or any other part of you needs more attention. With a Western Diagnosis often your life can be and will be saved by the interventions that can be done, but the actual quality of your daily life and health can be radically enhanced by working with an Integrated Medical practitioner.

The Liver cleanse by Sandra Cabot will also help hugely with Gallbladder issues.

The Good Back Guide by Barrie Savory D.O. is worth having on your bookshelf, as it full of incredibly important integrated information about our structure.

Summary of the Gallbladder chapter

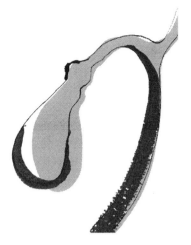

The Gallbladder is associated with the Spring Season

The element is Wood

The colour is green

The sound is shouting

The odour is rancid

The emotion/energy is anger/ frustration

The function of this organ is decision making

The associated organ is liver (Chapter 6)

Balanced Spring provides the ability to :

- Assert ourselves appropriately in the world

- Have structures and boundaries in order that the path can unfold

- Make plans and decisions

- Have a vision clearly of the unique path in your life

Behaviours that can become evident when the Spring energy is out of balance. These are the extremes that can become evident in ourselves and others.

Assertive and direct	to	passive and indirect
Rigid	to	over-flexible
Excessively organised	to	disorganised
Frustrated and defiant	to	over-obedient and compliant

Chapter 6

Discover your

Liver

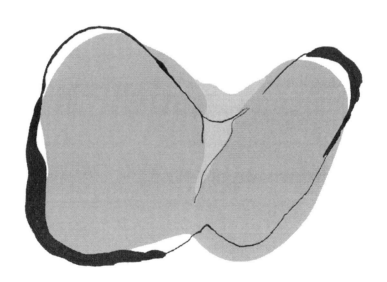

Sexuality becomes integrated with our Spirituality

Liver energy - Your planner

Emotions- anger, frustration

Strategy is derived from the health of your liver functioning and energy.

"How dare she invade my space and energetic field, as if we are already lovers? I am happily married and intend to remain so. One woman is quite enough for me".

"Honestly, I have done martial arts all of my life and thought I had understood about the power of our thoughts, our energy and our intention, but one meeting with this woman and I am all over the shop. Have you got a clue what I am going on about? I hope so. I cannot get her out of not only my mind but, more than that, out of my own energetic field. To my knowledge, I have not asked her in on any level.

"Sure, there was immediate chemistry and physical attraction, but I guess I have learned over the years just to witness that, not taking action because my senior equipment says so."

With a wry smile, knowing how and what to say to hold steady with the force of the energetic frustration in the treatment room, I responded to the staccato type barking. "Good morning! I hear that you have had a challenging week?"

Being in a room with this man was a bit like playing a powerful game of fast and good tennis. His energy was sending spinning balls in my direction in the hopes that A) I would understand, B) have a decent dialogue and possible energetic support for him, and possibly C) an explanation of what on earth was going on. He was clearly rattled.

The next patient on the same day:

"My nails are falling apart. My eyes are blurry and even floaters are flicking across my vision now. I am so tense, with slight discomfort in my chest and under my ribs. I am angry the entire time and so frustrated with everyone and everything. I'm on the brink of bursting into tears with periods that now are hellishly full of cramps and clotting blood. When my husband comes near me to be affectionate or even to instigate making love, I am just an angry grumpy baggage. Not exactly a turn on for either of us, really."

Another patient's opening sentences:

"I am belching with regurgitation going on all of the time, very particularly and embarrassingly in the middle of meetings I am taking. My staff look at me as if I am mad and rude. I am usually really dynamic and know the direction I want my company to go in. Now, suddenly I honestly don't seem to have a clue. Am I depressed? My wife says I am. Oh, and as for our sex life, which has always been great, I am now unable to get it together at all. That alone, mind you, is enough to have me depressed, but it is not that, I don't think. I still fancy my wife all of the time."

These were three patients who immediately, before I had asked more than the initial opening question, "How can I help?" had told me that their liver functioning was unhappy.

Our liver, within what we call our spring energy strongly affects our emotional life and alongside the dual aspects of our spirituality which is deeply rooted in our sexuality.

153

To the second patient, I asked the following questions:

"Is there anything that has recently happened that has made you furious and also confused?"

"Yes, my father-in-law is having an affair I have discovered; he knows that I now know and is wanting me to hush it all up as still no one else knows. He shows no respect or remorse, only an apparent obsessive need to carry on with the deceit."

"It's what my Dad did to my mom. I am livid but cannot yet talk to my wife without knowing what my plan is. It's a relief to tell you about it, in fact I already feel less tense. I was so wound up with a plumb sensation stuck in my throat. It was taking everything I had to not snap at our dear children. On the way here, some idiot cut across me, nearly crashing into me. My own instant rage frightened me more than the idiot. I am not myself at all. Like a pressure cooker just about to go off".

"I've even noticed that I am so tense that probably if I use exercise to burn off my frustration, I will pull a tendon. I've done that enough in my youth so I am damned if I am going to allow that tomfoolery of my equally idiotic father-in-law to get the better of me. Can you do something to release the pressure?

"Also, my mojo has gone from underneath me. I have no energy and I'm lethargic when I am not furious.

"I have also noticed the sense of trust and faith in something more than the surface that we can all get so affected by has been really shaken. I don't know what or who God is, but I have had plenty of experience to know that our spirits are connected to something far bigger than we normally talk about."

His last sentence allowed me to do a very particular treatment to open up more of what is possible for us all when we are ready in our own essence, spirit. As we are trained to see only potential in all the issues that we sooner or later have in our lives, it was my job to see the opportunity in this real life and potentially explosive situation. So, the dilemma he was in was also a chance for him to grow into what the situation would catalyse. We had a chat about how he might want to handle the situation, so that he left with a plan that would begin to work. With the benevolence and softness that can come from a very clear liver energy, this patient was able to see what was deeply behind his father-in-law's actions. Then, he could confront it in ways that did bring some clarity. He put some clear boundaries up and assertively used his position of knowing what was happening to talk through what the real consequences were going to be. His father-in-law had not even remotely thought through what was happening. He had been just diagnosed as diabetic and had taken it very hard; he was depressed and not seeing any way out of this youth slipping away.

As my patient was able and willing to learn more about his liver from a deeper perspective, he was able to plan and discern how to handle a potentially impossible situation. Alongside this work, we were also able to transform my patient's fury as we smoothed out the emotional frustration and rage he was triggered into. He separated what was to do with the present dilemma and the hurt still caught in his cells from his own father's behaviour and then found more compassion for his father-in-law. What he called his mojo came back, and his happy sex life continued again.

The functions of the liver, in part, "opens into the eyes," nourishes the tendons, manifests in the nails and ensures the smooth flow of emotions. So, it was not too far a stretch for his mind-sets to take on board that his internal vision needed to be shifted – shifted from his childhood experience to now giving his father-in-law a chance and, on as neutral a level as possible, to unravel some deep rooted unhappiness that was acting its way out in his behaviour. As he developed in to more of the potential we all have, he began to "see" with his spiritual eyes and perception.

With the true nature of our shared humanity, we begin to "see" beyond the reactive actions of others or indeed ourselves and actually "see" what is really happening. Therefore, we are then able to bend and be flexible with well oiled "tendons" on all the levels that the liver and our own tendons allow for in our movements.

In seeking a form of justice for his extended family, my patient needed to take the opportunity to work with the nitty-gritty reality of the problem facing his father-in-law and therefore the entire family. The father-in-law was acting out sexually from his spirit feeling and being clobbered on all sorts of levels. Increasingly, the more his son-in-law, my patient was willing to discern, without packing his thinking with judgment, what was actually beginning to make sense to him, a plan popped out organically. The father-in-law was also able to restore parts of his own childhood in ways that he actually hadn't known was unconsciously affecting the way he was interacting with his own family. The patient, in his willingness to work with the layers of what was happening, was able to affect not just himself in what potentially was a massive drama brewing. He was able to divert it and help everyone out.

"I seem able to be much more rooted in the bigger picture, which is what ultimately my own father-in-law has responded to. He was able to understand that he was operating momentarily from his own hurt, confusion and sense of what he perceived was his impending decline."

Bamboo is often associated with the nature of our internal wood energy, liver and gallbladder being the two associated energetic states. Healthy bamboo is rooted, empty and flexible for the winds to come. Its strength in the winds is to go with them and yet not get ultimately diverted from its direction of growth and evolution, which is its internal healthy inclination. It does not take it personally when the winds whistle, rage and storm through wherever it is. By taking everything personally, we fight against our true natures, adding much more stress on our clever systems that are actually designed to become increasingly empty, or still from the middle out and then importantly unattached, yet rooted so that we continue to develop our potential through the storms that we will all contend with.

When we are constantly taking everything personally and reacting in frustration and anger to everything around us, we begin to have internal wind building in our own systems that leads to strokes and heart attacks. Like the winds in nature that can suddenly stir up the waters quickly and cause havoc in an unpredictable manner, our own behaviour can become unpredictable, rapid and erratic, whereas healthy and righteous anger is flowing in ways that support our growth. We begin to become less belligerent and also less timid with our own unique path and with the need for personal growth.

So, if you take a moment to think through making love the nature of our movements and our ability to respond to another's needs, flexibility becomes paramount for transcending the pitfalls of building intimacy.

The more we are willing to see with our own inner and outer vision with a healthy liver and strong functioning spring energy, the better we can become intimate with the needs of ourselves and others. We all know the odd mismatching that goes on in life, rather like one moment the wind is howling uncomfortable around our necks and the next it has suddenly died down. A connection will take us by the scruff of our necks, shake us so that we feel utterly senseless one moment so that we can hardly think of anything else; then, just as suddenly, the person who has momentarily rocked our world goes from being lit up by us to apparently turning cold on us. The electric circuit that was running so vibrantly one moment between two people can suddenly get sporadic and as non-responsive to us as previously it was responsive. It is in part and hugely the liver that produces the smooth flowing of that emotional and energetic currency between the outer world and inner world. So, when we are developing the dual aspects of our spirituality and sexuality, gradually our own behaviour becomes more congruent and fluid in all aspects.

My father, who painted people, landscapes and houses, for a living, took me aside when he thought the time was right with this wisdom which, in hindsight, sums up this chapter.

"When you find someone attractive physically and you respond sexually to that initial impulse, it is like taking a hammer to kill a gnat. It may not always be a wise move to respond to such powerful and never-to-be underestimated stimuli."

The two biggest internal responses that we have to our lives is the constant flow or possible stagnation of our sexual and spiritual natures. They are so bound up with everything that to downgrade them to merely a physical act in the name of sex is missing the energetic exchanges that take place. It is said that for a woman to have a man inside her means that she carries his energy with her for 7 years. So, having casual sex or what is termed "fuck buddies" is based on an extremely narrow understanding of what is actually taking place during the act of sex. Whereas the art of love making and intimacy is a life times dance with much more than satiating desire or sensation. Mastering desire, physical impetus, for ourselves let alone another is a journey of endless exploration into how vulnerable we are.

On the one hand, whilst so immensely capable of what being a lover fully is. Orgasms can bring our bodies to increasing levels of bliss that of course it is natural to want more of, but not beginning to understand the full potential of what our bodies are capable of can hamper our potential from developing.

Equally, to believe that learning a form of meditation or doing weekend courses on our spiritual aspects is going to get us through the hoops of a lifetime's undertaking is limiting. The fantasies that we can be "fixed" of our deep yearnings, frustrations and longings in a weekend is a worldly setup that causes much more of what got us going on the "fixes" in the first place. To be lulled into believing that life is anything other than an incredible adventure in experiences that either will or will not allow us as individuals to come home to ourselves, will play into our added sense of what is wrong rather then what is right with us. Instead, the seasons ultimately do lead us to find a real contentment.

Although ongoing daily disciplines that keep us focused on our own internal journey are necessary and powerful ways for us to become much more conscious. They will have the potential to serve our dual aspects, of interconnecting our often mismatched behaviour with what we say we want, then in ways that liberate us. It is of vital importance that when we have some sort of daily routine that we understand what its long term goal, intention or potential is to us, rather than merely following a fashion. We need to be engaged with the process so that truly we can experience the greater results in our daily interactions with each other. There are so many ways in which we can evolve, so it is important to know which really suits our energetic make-up and how we uniquely respond to differing teachings or disciplines. Some people walk in prayer, literally, and are not sit-down-quietly people; instead, they make their whole lives a prayer. Others adore sitting for hours quietly and can do silent retreats for days. The more you learn about yourself, the more you will know what you need. The key though is always down to how you are developing in all aspects of your own being. I cannot even tell you how many patients over the years seem to practise something that they never ever stop to ask themselves if it is a supportive or constructive daily exercise. Often they begin to wake up themselves to some ritual of fashion just not working for them.

A friend jumped a very long queue with me the other day. I have often to use my walking stick and was having a particularly nasty time with pain. Taking a look at a long, winding staircase up and then down to where eventually we would be seated, she kindly took charge and politely asked if we could be accepted into the queue, halfway down, thereby saving me what, in fact, I would not on that occasion have been able to do. What was amusing, though, was that most of the people, waiting to hear one of the leading Spiritual teachers of our day, would have probably considered themselves part of an enlightened group of people. In direct contrast, however, to any real enlightenment, the fuss that spun out and around us as we were belligerently accepted into the queue was actually funny. People all around us held onto resentments and a rigid series of judgements, so much so that I suspect none of them even saw my walking stick. They were far more comfortable to sit in their indignant fury at two people queue jumping than to see and discern what was going on. It was such a small but very telling example of what we can all do. We can so easily become quite self-righteous around our meditations, prayers or differing acts of spiritual growth and yet when actually faced with being compassionate or flexible we fall at the first hurdle daily. I certainly do endlessly, but equally endlessly I am able to also acknowledge where I am being changed by my own choice of disciplines that help me to become more integrated from the inside out.

It is our liver energy, though, that roots our theory of life into the actual practise of it. A healthy wood energy will be incredibly kind and not too self-righteous. Through the power of liver, we can be moderate around the need to rest and be also active in our days. We can express the energy around our frustrations and our emotional states in healthy ways, allowing for each turn of our own Spring energy to propel us into more personal growth, a growth that will allow for the internal integration between our sexuality and our spirituality.

The nature of anger within our liver, wood energy is expressed as very dynamic assertion but with great clarity. It will assert itself as a shoot, which is even capable in Spring of somehow finding its way through concrete. So, we know our liver is in balance when we are able to respond to life and its endless frustrations by having equilibrium with flexibility that keeps us in a state of inner harmony, focused with our own internal strategy. We will remain structured in our days but not overly so, capable of putting boundaries up. We know the absolute difference between our "no" and our resistance to something that has to be faced and leaned into for us to continue our journey. Many people need to deliberately learn to do what they do not want to, to challenge themselves to let go of their comfort zones. Exercises like these take people back into their own dynamic life force. Others, however, need to be allowed to actually create a comfort zone for themselves if their lives have been too much like a continual assault course.

So, now back to my first patient of the day who was so rattled.

He was glaring at me, or, more accurately, sort of through me, waiting for me to be a channel for some sort of enlightened discussion.

It always makes me almost giggle inside myself when I know something is now expected of me that I equally know that I do not necessarily, or even at all, have access to, at least not right away. I have learned to relax totally and allow something far greater than my endless limits to arrive in the next ensuing moments. Although, in the next thing that came out of my mouth, I am not sure who was more surprised - the patient or myself.

"Have you ever heard of sacred prostitution?"

The question had snapped him into the present moment in under a heartbeat. Now, the glare was in full force - AT me.

"Okay, smack that between my eyeballs please, as it has for sure got my attention. In fact, so much so that I suddenly feel alert and at peace, so you are on to something."

That is the incredible privilege of working with people at very intense and sometimes vulnerable places. They totally entrust you with their realities without any of the masks that are used mostly in our normal days, bar the few exceptions that live without them.

"Caroline Myss, in her work on our archetypes, refers to the Alchemist within us as both the light attribute "transformation of base motives and goals into golden wisdom," or, on the shadow attribute, "misuse of the power and knowledge that come through spiritual practise".

"She also refers to prostitution as the activating of the unconscious related to seduction and control, whilst also as selling or selling-out of talents, ideas and other expression of the self, added to which referring to the need to birth and refine self-esteem and self-respect".

"The 'shadow prostitute' assesses all transactions only in terms of how they profit you and not what they will cost you spiritually."

"So, it seems to me that you are alchemizing your own next step by responding to a distress signal from this woman. You will be the only person within her immediate vicinity that is capable of not responding from the most base level to her own muddled energy. So, sacred prostitution is the alchemy involved in truly transforming what is in front of you with another person that is rocking your world. Intellectually, you know that they are not right for you or you for them, yet you still have the energy between you both demanding to be seen, heard and met in some form. It is literally your highest note of needing to give birth to your own next step, which is integrating more your spirituality with your sexuality, whilst also in service to another when you will not be making love to this woman sexually. You already sense what spiritual suicide that would be which is partly why you are so fired up. That is also totally separate for this moment in time from the passion that you have for your family and wife. However, on a spiritual level you need to humbly be willing to go through a sacred dance ritual very consciously with this woman."

"Being part of one of your classes, she will continue to be under your nose three times a week, so you will have ample time to master this, however tricky it seems. As with all the other transformations you have gone through, you will also master this. This is when your own Prince archetype goes from being the Prince to the King. This woman has never been honoured for more than her sexuality, which she now uses as a badge of honour but is longing for her own being to be more than a sex object. She does not have a clue of her own value, does she? That is what the invitation is, which you can sense for yourself by your own responses to what I am saying. If it resonates, which it clearly is, your mind, body and spirit immediately respond."

"Wow, hold on for a second. How do you know that?"

"Your colour, sound and tone of voice are clearly giving me feedback. Also, it is a pattern that arises from our societies that simply do not know yet how to integrate the sacred masculine and feminine together, and you have already told me the story clearly with your energy."

"Oh, okay. Go on, as this sure is settling me. My energy is calming right down and although I am not fully grasping in my mind what you are saying, what I trust now is how my body feels and how my heart is settling."

"In terms of Caroline Myss's work, so that you can refer to it again and again, the lover within you has already matured into embracing what she calls, "unbridled appreciation of someone or something," from having been obsessive in your passions in the past - obsessive to the point where it hurt yourself and others. You then transformed that behaviour a long time ago. In your case, you have been for many years discovering through martial arts the joys of mastering your own energy. So, your passion about your relationship, your children and your own individual continued journey is bigger than your own 'senior equipment's responses to another woman,' as you call your penis."

"You are now being given the opportunity to serve this woman, one of your clients, in a very sacred way: consciously giving of yourself in clear intention to the pursuit of her unfolding and without using your sexuality in all the ways that as a younger man you may have. The chemistry, energy between you will settle hugely once you have truly got into what the energetic signs were telling you. That then keeps you clear in your integrity and intention. You are evolving into more self-trust around very demanding situations"

"This is just another opportunity to go to the next level of understanding. Whilst your sexuality integrates with your spirituality, there will always be the chances to serve another way beyond the level that they feel worthy of. As you yourself experienced being at the mercy of your obsessive nature and then was able to transform to a form of detachment and healthy expressions of your love, you now get to read someone else's deeper longing. When such powerful chemistry comes up that requires or even demands some sort of dance, if we are not careful it can so easily be totally misunderstood."

"As the integration becomes deeper and embedded in an everlasting sacred experience, it becomes more difficult to go against your own bigger purpose, which will always be to serve the whole. Sacred men and women throughout history have unfolded the great mysteries of the dual aspects of our joint sexuality and spirituality. When it is being misused, it hijacks individuals into a merry-go-round of more self-deception and far greater suffering. The self-deception is easy to even smell as the wood energy gets rigid, defended and harsh, and loud, brash even."

He was fascinated by the integrated nature of our sexuality and spirituality. He began to talk much more openly about how he had "matured" to wanting to "make love" to the woman he loved, "making sure she was pleasured, rather than the focus at first being satisfying my most basic instinct."

"I never realised how powerful lovemaking could be and what it actually did to the two of us the more we were willing to be intimate with each other. It was truly terrifying at first as I was so focused on being right, being in charge, hiding myself from everyone, including my chosen partner. I hadn't at all learned or even conceived the notion that my basic instinct would alter or evolve, so now I automatically can see a stunningly attractive woman walk past and I don't any longer want to possess and devour her. It is not that all my fantasies have gone, but more like I am now the master of all of myself, rather than my 'lower half' constantly dictating to me. Before, I was controlled by sensation really, constantly chasing a form of instant gratification. I was so easily sexually aroused that I had so many incredibly embarrassing times when I was younger - having erections at the worst times. I really fancied my math teacher and if she ever addressed me I would burn in more ways than one."

"I was obsessed with porn for a long while until as I began Martial arts, the empty burning, as I knew it by, that only got worse the more I had allowed myself to get sucked into an increasingly sordid world, began to be 'less empty.' I had a great teacher who actually talked kindly and informatively about the world he had known that I was stuck in. There was never any judgment; in fact, the reverse, as he understood the biological and spiritual nature of what I had been seeking. Overuse of masturbation, or porn and treating women as objects just for a quick fix was going to exacerbate the energy that actually needed to be mastered, rather than taking me down such unfulfilling paths. He explained that when we are not teaching our young men about their own sexuality, power in the masculine and how to utilise their own energy, then it backfires into all sorts of acting out. I see now women being encouraged to treat us now as objects of instant gratification also"

"I love the work that I now do with young guys showing them the healthier, energetic choices that we can have around our sexuality and then ultimately the integration between our own powerful essence, spirituality and the sacred in our sexuality, which then, of course, leads to much more deeply satisfying life choices, relationships and real intimacy on all levels".

As he talked what had begun as one simple sentence began to merge into what was already within his own grasp of being and becoming. As practitioners it is our job to be empty enough of ourselves to allow the patient to begin to have space for that next step to be experienced, that is already in them. We have that possibility within us layer by layer as we take steps to become more conscious and aware of our own beings.

When we are younger and not having any real outlets for our creative, sexual and dynamic life force, then of course it can all go down increasingly unpleasant hidden and then ultimately shame-driven avenues.

In this chapter, I have stuck to relevant examples to the chapter heading, but to end I want to give you more of a picture of what your incredibly clever liver is doing for you all of the time. It is described in Chinese Medicine as your "army's general from whom the strategy is derived."

The liver has two clear strategies that each support the other whilst then supporting your navigational system. Whilst storing blood for rest and activity, and menstruation, it also is ensuring the smooth flow of your energy for your emotions, your digestion and the secretion of bile.

The blood, in turn, nourishes the tendons and manifests in your nails. It is described as "opening into the eyes" and houses the hun, the unique energy of the liver. The hun is like the root of your own spring energy. So, if you imagine your own garden, for instance, in the Spring trying to develop without being properly rooted, that is what the root, or hun, does.

So, people who make plans but cannot quite ever bring them fully into the fruition stage are sometimes not rooted. You can imagine from the list of its uses in your own body how much the liver is doing. There are many conditions in the treatment room that we see and know are based on what we call blood deficient, which very basically means that the quality of your blood, which you need to be rich and strong, is showing signs of what would be considered to be anaemia. So, when you notice that you are sort of wishy washy about plans and are "all over the shop" emotionally, you may want to have a look at your own diet. I will give you all sorts of tips to just think through about your liver. They are pointers to consider. In no way do they mean, though, that you can avoid having proper bloodwork done and be taking active responsibility for your well-being with the help of a qualified doctor or medical practitioner.

The liver function, when balanced, is staying between the following possible imbalances:

Assertive and direct	Passive and indirect
Seeking justice	Apathetic
Rigid	Over-flexible
Excessively organised	Disorganised
Frustrated and defiant	Over=obedient and compliant

As anger is the emotion associated with what we call your Spring energy, your wood, it is so important to begin to unpack for yourselves what your associations are with your anger. Without the energy of what anger appropriately can do for you, we all can get caught out by our anger and frustrations having us in control, rather than us in charge of our own dynamic life force, which will always include our anger. Anger used wisely and turned to appropriate levels of assertion is paramount to our life force evolving and dynamically so.

Unglamorous tips for glamorous living or tantalizing teasers

These are random tips and more brush stroke pointers if you want to go further with these subjects. They are not in any particular order.

- A book by Greg Lampert and Danny Blyth called 'Eating for Health and Wellbeing; has fantastic information around eating and food in connections to the seasons. Pages 26-27 are about Wood patterns.

When our Wood/Spring energy is out of balance we need often what we call blood nourishing foods. I list only a few here as it is always imperative that you find an excellent practitioner to work with you and to help you unravel your own individual needs if and when you are at dis-ease.

- Liver pate
- Red wine
- Dandelion
- Apricots
- Dark leafy vegetables
- Bone marrow.

Angela and John Hicks have a book called 'Healing Your Emotions' and is a brilliant book full of more information on your seasons and masses of practical exercises. They were two of my favourite teachers because they lived what they taught us.

Although there are now a lot of books on sexual techniques it is important with this level of integration that you find teachers, books or information that know about the Alchemy of these subjects. The blending of the two forces within you can be a lifetime's work, which will be in charge of you until you become conscious enough to be in charge of them.

So the next tip is, if you are well enough. Experiment with exercise around:

- Kickboxing
- Tai-chi
- Dancing, particularly ones where you will be challenged to come into your own body and sexuality.
- Exercise routines where you are really moving your body.
- Anything that gets you into your body and out of your mind where we now mostly inhabit our days, which our integrated energy does not like.

If you begin to identify that you are living with a lot of frustration find a way of letting out the frustrations in creative ways that do not backfire. Usually the liver needs movement rather than lack of movement to settle the energy. Find out why your levels of frustration are high. Is your dynamic life force and creativity being overly challenged or not expressed?

If you recognise you have problems with depressions and moods that keep altering this is a useful book :

- 'The Mood Cure' by Julia Ross

Once again, please seek help to establish what the underlying cause is. What is your clever body telling you? Be honest with yourself about your bodies sign posts.

CONSTANTLY ask yourself when you recognise that you are stuck, depressed or out of sorts :

"Is this from my mind, body or essence? What do I need or do I need to go through this kindly and gently, wisely?" Be willing to seek support and help from someone who will and can get it, without necessarily medicating only the signs posts, not dealing with the real cause. Make sure you find your roots, the roots of the dis-ease. The symptoms and signs are guiding you, so be aware of constantly either trying to run from them, shut them up or drown them. Again and again the boomerang effect will come back at you. What you do, put out, think, act and be comes straight back at you.

Dr Sandra Cabot has two books I have used extensively over the years on cherishing our livers, on the physical level, so they are well worth looking at. Keeping your liver clean will have dramatic effects on your thinking, moods and behaviour. Go to your local library and have a look at them first. Better for you than using your liver energy on a computer screen to check it out!

- The Liver Cleanse
- The Healthy Liver And Bowel Book

Get enough sleep. If you or anyone else believes that regularly not getting enough rest and proper sleep is ok then they simply do not know about the real needs of our livers, for starters.

Please practise winding down at 9pm, NO MORE computer lights near you after that at the very latest. It is better to switch everything off far earlier.

Take TV's, computers, any gadgets out of your sleeping area.

As Dr. Mosley said correctly in his 'Clever Guts' book

"Your bedroom is for rest, sleep and sex" nothing else.

Of course there are masses of people that do not have that luxury of being able to cherry pick where to have things, but if you want a healthier liver working with you then be creative. SWITCH OFF EVERYTHING AT 9pm. Cover over ANY lights that your precious eyes will still focus on if visible. If you are scientific minded please do the research on how damaging all this magnetic resonance is on our bodies.

When I stay in hotels that have all sorts of blinking fire alarms and fluorescent lighting, I will go to great lengths to find ways of shutting them out of my vision so that the quality of my sleep will be far better than if I had not bothered.

Watch the news or stimulating TV early on in the evenings. NOT ever the 10:00pm slot. You will be sure it is not affecting you but I can assure you it is. Do not take my word for it though. Experiment with these ideas for the sake of your own wellbeing.

Keep your bowels working which is in the Large Intestine chapter, which will help the liver hugely

A glorious book that may be a soothing night time and gentle look through is

- The Tantra Experience, Osha

The following books will be mentioned several times as they cross over inevitably with the integration of your needs.

- 'What Your Body Is Telling You, and what you can do about it', by David Rowland. Canada's foremost expert in Holistic nutrition. He also published 'Nutritiapedia', the free online nutritional encyclopaedia. Whilst also being the creator of the Nutri body system used by natural health practitioners for determining nutritional and biochemical weaknesses. He is an extraordinary fountain of abundant knowledge with the brain the size of the cosmos which he fully utilizes for the sake of mankind.

- 'The Dynamic Laws of Prayer' by Catherine Ponder is a clever exploration of the power behind prayer.

- 'The Intention Experiment' By Lynn Mctaggart is a fascinating read, as she refers to herself "a hardnosed journalist who did not believe in anything but hard core facts and science". If you can ever go to one of her lectures then you will be in for a very stimulating listening. You do not have to agree with everything but allow your liver the stimulation of listening and SEEING someone who is out in the world really exploring and discovering what IS POSSIBLE.

Ask for help in working out what your unique path is in life. It may change but allow yourself the luxury of bothering to define a clear vision.

Make plans and decisions based on keeping your energy passionately engaged through your seasons. Align yourself with the seasons outside of yourself and step by gentle step you will experience the quality of your days to be changing. Let your levels of frustration guide you as to what next. Be kind to your frustrations and listen to what they are saying.

Look to yourself through the eyes of your own Hun Energy, kindly and wisely as your evolving unravels through each and every level of dis-ease.

Deliberately switch off noise and activities around you, learn to practise being still and quiet to begin to know how to refuel yourself without endless outside interruptions. Wean yourself off your mobile devices by fasting from them!.

Barrie Savory who has been my osteopath since I was in my early teens has written a book called The Good Back Guide. It is beautifully written by a man that is still passionate about his work and the human body. He also concludes this book. So if you have any structural issues please remember how very effective cranial, osteopathic and chiropractic treatments are before you seek out surgical options. As an aside be very mindful that when a knee problem arrives it is worth having the alignment of your hips checked first to see if that is impacting your knee.

Nothing is separate so start to think of connections as everything is interconnected and linked up.

Lastly but vitally if you are frightening yourself, let alone others with your temper, if not uncontrollable rages or tantrums please seek help. You need to learn to manage what is driving your rage. If it has gone on for quite some time then it can easily have become a threefold issue, chemical, emotional and even spiritual. There are even meetings you can go to learn how to manage your rage. Everyone around you will mostly be too afraid to ask you to seek help. For yours and everyone's sake pick up the phone or see your doctor and tell them that you are increasingly losing all control of your constantly boiling pot of rages inside yourself.

Summary of the Liver chapter

Liver

The liver is associated with the Spring Season

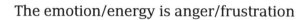

The element is Wood

The colour is green

The sound is shouting

The odour is rancid

The emotion/energy is anger/frustration

The function of this organ is planning.

The associated organ is gallbladder (Chapter 5)

A Balanced Spring provides the ability to:

- Assert ourselves appropriately in the world

- Have structures and boundaries in order that the path can unfold

- Make plans and decisions

- Have a vision clearly of the unique path in your life

Behaviours that can become evident when the Spring energy is out of balance. These are the extremes that can become evident in ourselves and others.

Assertive and direct	to	passive and indirect
Rigid	to	over-flexible
Excessively organised	to	disorganised
Frustrated and defiant	to	over-obedient and compliant
Seeking justice	to	Apathetic

Chapter 7

Discover your

Thermostat

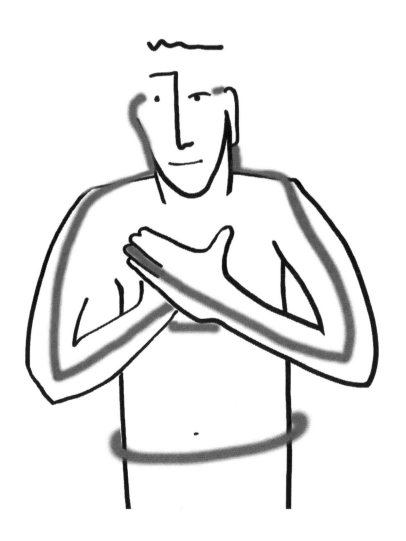

Laughing With Self, Lightly Tossed - Triple Burner / Thermostat

The element is FIRE

"She is not available. I have played this game for so long enough that I want to figure out my part in it. Sometimes I think I am attracted only to unavailable women. If they were actually open to a decent long term relationship I think honestly I would run a mile."

"Real intimacy terrifies me. I can be all over someone like a rash one moment and then suddenly cold if they actually respond".

"I keep so many friendships going on all at once in a sort of frothy bubbling way but make damn sure no one gets too close. I never have one on ones with anyone"

"I run hot and cold all the time"

These types of remarks from patients over the years would have me wondering about the state of their triple burner, thermostat within the Summer Fire energy. They are all indications that the thermostat is not working at a steady and even temperature.

Our summer season within us, the official of balance and harmony, has four distinct energy systems that all harmonize our fire energy. The triple burner, which I will refer to as your thermostat, is your first line of defence in your body's fire system.

Imagine that your heart is the Queen, or King of your own internal kingdom. If you think about Buckingham Palace, there are many lines of protection and defence before anyone can get near the Queen of England. On the outer edges of your own Buckingham Palace is your first line of protection, your thermostat energy that will decide if it is appropriate to allow someone in further or closer to your heart. The functioning of a balanced thermostat is constantly assessing potential damage that could invade your own inner sanctuary where the heart is governing your whole body.

Within your own navigational system you have three distinct but interlinking security systems that are what we call the summer season, your Fire. These are the small intestine, Pericardium, and then our heart. As in the illustration, part of the security lay out is on the outer edges of your arms. These systems ensure that at all times your throne-heart, is kept safe and guarded, whilst the thermostat maintains homeostasis by regulating the water and fire in your system. It is responsible for the constant gathering of all the information that is necessary for the heart to govern consistently and well, maintaining temperatures that stay steady throughout the many changes going on around it. When in balance, and working steadily on our behalf, intimacy is spontaneous and without conscious thought.

To describe what your fire energy system is like will not just stretch my descriptive writing but equally your imagination. Hopefully, you will have gained much more insight into how your systems within your body and its organs work so to now add another layer to your own interlinking systems may be easier. You may have even begun to experience your days differently. Once you begin to understand that you have an incredible network that is being influenced by your choices, actions, thinking, and belief systems, you can begin to steer your energy differently. As you gain more insight, life itself can really begin to feel and be lighter, even with the toughest of situations.

It is your own summer season/your fire that will actually respond with fun, laughter and merriment to life on a daily basis, and is deeply connected to your interactions with others.

Have you ever noticed that when talking about subjects that you love you get "fired up?" When we are watching a play, ballet, film or sport there is animation written all over our faces. Watch people's' reactions when an attractive person walks into a room or when someone pays another attention. Sexual chemistry is presumed to be, and is marketed as being, solely based on rather superficial criteria. However, in reality, when a person is animated and in their own authority, they can be very magnetic to all of life. When the internal fire is strong the magnetic force between people is usually very easy to feel, see and hear; on all levels it is obvious. Then there are people who literally know how to turn the switch on or off, to their own magnetic force field.

Marilyn Monroe was said to be walking with a friend in New York when his asked how it was possible that they were not being bothered by anyone, as if she was not being recognised. Apparently, she explained that she knew how to literally switch her magnet/ inner light on, so as she wanted to be alone with her friend she had it off. He did not believe her so she gave him a choice. If he wanted to see her switch it on, then he had to accept that their private time was going to be over as they would get mobbed quickly. He naturally said that he wanted to see for himself what she was talking about. The story ends with them being mobbed within 20 minutes as she flicked the switch on.

Like Marilyn Monroe, we all have that facility to flip our switch on or off no matter what our outward appearance is, or no matter what the circumstances are. Although at times women all over the world know what it is like to be in a sort of clunky mood where nothing goes right as they cannot activate the switch to on. Part of evolving and maturing is discovering that we do have switches inside of us that we can consciously operate with integrity. Men equally know automatically when they have to switch off and go into their man cave to revitalize themselves, or they need to go to the pub for instance. As the fire is usually refuelled by company it is important to choose the right type of interaction that is needed.

Imagine having an ignition switch to light the Fire or the gas in our homes that is what we can learn to do increasingly. A very clear example of this is the following scenario.

A person rings us who we know in the middle of us doing something. We answer the phone even though we actually do not want to talk at that moment. If we answer in the first place, we can decide to be warm, in our voice instead of cold and rushed. The more we can consciously become aware of our actions the more we all can make choices about how we are with the inside of our worlds and the outside. The world is crying out for far more warmth to be shared, which does come from us being more balanced in our Fire, and therefore choices.

The issues arising from literally putting the heating on too high or letting our homes get too cold as we never put on our heating is similar to our own navigational systems. We need to know how and when to turn up the controls, but more in an automatic way rather than overriding the system with a sense of control. So in the case of comedians, who for instance, can take full control of an audience, seeming to be very intimate with them, yet, if you meet them outside of their arena they may appear aloof and very different.

There has to be a sense of consistent balance for the thermostat to support the heart.

The following are just some of the physical symptoms that can arise from the Triple Burner energy not being in harmony:- Heart palpitations, agitation, insomnia, dream disturbed sleep, easily startled, spontaneous sweating, feeling of cold or heat.

Imagine what would happen if there was no policing going on around our hearts, or our own cities, or simply not enough policing anywhere at all. This is, in fact, what is becoming a reality now in some places, so crime is being committed as the gangs know exactly what they can get away with. For example, the headline on one newspaper as I write is: *"60 moped muggings a day as police fear copycat crime spree".* The gangs' individual fires are all over the place as they increasingly get "fired up," and get "kicks" out of a sense of belonging, connection and warmth that only superficially fuels their deep longings. They are not interested in or able to distinguish between what they need beyond blatant survival. So, if selling drugs or being involved in petty crime initially, then advancing to more serious crimes, leads to an initial sense of validation and warmth within their own peer group, then the price they are paying will initially seem worth it.

Societies leave themselves wide open by not figuring out what we collectively are doing with the literal fire in the bellies of our young. Are we extinguishing the fires of our next generations too young or are we putting individuals and families in systems that blatantly do no longer work? With absent fathers and even mothers now, children are just not getting the time, care and attention that the fire needs, initially and regularly, to keep them stoked up continually. Our fires will do whatever it takes to keep our embers going, however inappropriate it seems on the outside.

As an example, one of the above patients had to honestly face all the tough, early experiences he had had. His behaviour, choices and decisions around connections and relationships had become either too guarded, or too inappropriately open. For instance, on the one hand he was allowing untrustworthy people beyond his inner guards, making it difficult to expel them from his kingdom, leaving himself way too open to protect himself. Then on the other hand he was keeping safe and consistently warm and loving people at bay.

He was burnt up inside at a very early age and not able to protect himself. It was as if his guards at the gates of his own inner sanctuary had been overwhelmed; those very guards were unable to do the job that they are supposed to do. His heart had closed off with the sheer velocity of the blows that he had received on multiple levels by people, events and consequences that were stacking up like a rolling avalanche. He was longing for intimacy, closeness and validation on the outside when, in fact, he was sending out all the wrong signals from embers inside himself that had very nearly gone out. However, equally those very embers would erratically suddenly burst into flames and give false senses of unsustainable warmth to others. So, it was imperative for his own well-being that he began to have a serious review of his own energy states. It would have been all too easy to get stuck into a vicious cycle of the focus being on what was done to him in childhood, rather than dealing with the stark consequences of his own ongoing responses to a deeply confusing childhood.

Whitewashing the challenges with quick and ultimately futile fixes only prolongs the discomfort and unresolved pain that, in the case of the fire, either produces a faltering thermostat or a raging, overheating one that has scalding water in its piping.

When we are desperate for warmth, we will grab with pure survival and adrenalized, if internalized, fear, whatever will make a fire. It then takes time to learn how to fuel the burning embers from sustainable interactions that keep us warm evenly and on all levels.

One of the first homework's that I gave this brave and honest man was to find people who he admired and who seemed to be able to have trustworthy intimate relationships. He was to observe from a distance what it looked and felt like. It had to be initially at a distance as it would have frightened him too much to be too close to it. I also wanted him to see if he could find examples of the rhythms of nature all around him. I asked him to watch nature programmes with a particular assignment of watching the courting rituals of many animals such as the dancing that goes on in the mating seasons. I did ask him not to go for the ones that end up eating their mate once they have made love. Chuckling to himself he said that he had never looked forward to a home work before. However he was intimidated, initially, by the other homework which was to explore dancing lessons.

There have been many people in the world who are so tuned into the rhythms of nature that they know within themselves when there is a new moon, or when the tide is in or out at any time of living near water. There are people who get headaches when it is going to snow. My father would feel the weather changing before it became apparent that it was. In Africa, where I had the privilege of living, we would smell when the rains were arriving. One of my most precious soul mates would be aware when a woman was in her menstrual cycle. He was so tuned into life that he knew exactly how to sense, to smell, to hear and to see what was happening in the Animal kingdom. It initially was a little intimidating, though, when, while walking past a woman, I was suddenly told at what point in her cycle the stranger was. The two men who moved my soul the most and who I have had the great honour of knowing and being with were integrated men of Nature and were like Crocodile Dundee, with humour and amusement that living with nature brings. There was a constant energy of adventure and excitement for each and every day being around both these men.

When our thermostat is in balance it is also partially maintaining the homeostasis for our receiving, processing and elimination. It

184

is said that one way of looking at the movement and life force in a relationship between the feminine and the masculine is to think of the seas. With the moving rhythms of two people living together it is easier to begin to understand that the feminine rhythm has a cyclical upward and downwards motion. Whilst the masculine has a horizontal ebbing and flowing movement.

So, when we get the hang of the rhythms of our own thermostat we can know when to just go with nature. For example, when the masculine energy seems to withdraw having been very intimate it is going back out to sea to regroup and will be back, while the feminine will be moving either on the downward wave, monthly cycles, or having regrouped, letting go and moving up to once again take on the world in an inspired and dynamic way. No wonder there are so many unpleasant misunderstandings going on around women's periods and men's needs and rhythms that need to be allowed without the confusions that we all can get into. Same sex connections can also be fraught with the need to find the rhythms and expressions between the internal feminine and masculine. All of which has an enormous impact on our fire energy

Male partners who truly respect and love women wholeheartedly know where to support their partner when they go into the depths of their winters, their downward movements, and are tired and fragile whilst literally blood is accumulating in their wombs with all the month's collective waste as it is leaving her body. Equally, these men know how to embrace her rhythms of being able to take on the world and go outwards more. He does not demand that she be different from the natural rhythm that is a part of the wealth of being female. Women, who feel secure within themselves, allow the man his equivalent dance.

Having had the experience of being with two men who really

respected and loved women, it was very liberating to be expected to keep moving and changing throughout each month. I was never called hysterical or emotional with nasty tones of disrespect. When I was tearful and in the cycle of feeling fragile and needing actually to slow up and respect what my body was doing, they both supported me. Equally, they loved it when I would come back up and out feeling stronger and clearer for the next month's demands. Then, also, it was my job to allow and embrace them in their rhythms.

Initially, I was simply hopeless at this dance of ever changing cycles. I was so out of rhythm and wanted attention when my first partner was way out to sea or simply would take it personally when, after love-making, he would get up and leave. He would potter around in our garden without me. Later, as he was a great communicator, he told me that actually he had had such a deep connection with me that he had been connected to an aspect of himself that he then needed to be with - alone. It actually was a huge compliment to what we were bravely attempting to build together. Once I got the hang of his rhythms, I would simply go to sleep, at peace and understanding. Sometimes, he would arrive an hour or so later with a tray of our favourite ritual of tea and some snack. We then would have hours of chatting about every single aspect of life. I do not believe that our relationship would have been as rich as it was if we did not have an increasing sense of each other's rhythms and the monthly cycles. As the life force within us was going to be expressed, we needed to become conscious of it and, "in joy" that nature was having her way in us and outside of us. I was blessed to be with masters of Nature and integration in ways that the average western person now is losing touch with.

Our relationships with others can improve immensely with just the art of laughing at ourselves, or being "lightly tossed," as I call it. Our summer season brings out that warmth and ability to not take too much too seriously.

So, if you are in a relationship and one or other of you is absent, with the TV on for instance, just check and see if in fact one of you is way out to sea or on a downward cycle ,switched off and / or fragile so tuning out.

It is our thermostat that smoothly contributes to a system that is now, in my own case, a massive part of how successfully I live alongside those conditions that are under the umbrella of the Ehlers-Danlos syndrome. My own thermostat produces balance and a sense of inner harmony, controlling the water passages and excretion of fluids. For a long time, just the ability to sweat became a luxury that my body no longer was able to facilitate which, in and of itself, had all sorts of consequences.

The previous patient's emotional volatility, confusion and sense of not being loveable was transformed into feeling mostly loveable, content, at home emotionally. His choices became warmer and more consistent with all of his interactions. He did not make so many absolute relationship pickles with his thermostat on duty once again.

He began to understand as he recovered through his grief of all the losses involved in not really having had a safe childhood that he would always be vulnerable in his Thermostat area, but that equally it could be his greatest asset and strength. None of his own particular journey though or that of anyone that I have ever worked with is ever "job done;" it is season by season. Watch nature and her cycles; we live with constant change and we, in balance, are constantly moving with nature, too. Our external thermostats need to be looked after and serviced alongside the heating and water systems regularly - we cannot afford to take them for granted.

Vitally, and importantly for our own well-being and sense of inner equilibrium, no matter what our circumstances or bodies are doing, we are able to take regular and consistent responsibility for our actions and behaviours, never blaming another which always means that we are able to be internally in a win-win situation. The sense of lightness and humour mostly ripples through our own internal kingdom when we truly get that we are the masters of our own switches.

The greatest privilege of my life was living with two darling children who, alongside their father, used to call anyone being a martyr a "tomato." So, to this day I can catch myself being absurd, with the caricature-type of brain I have, with my own ridiculous and very momentary antics. The equivalent of the hands on my hips, sighing and being bedraggled with my own script of martyred, doomsday, "stinking thinking," forecasting more than I actually have to handle in the moment, I can often burst out into the joy of laughter with myself. Hence, the name of this title as a healthy and mature fire will provide just enough warmth for a room to be comfortable - not too hot and not too cold. Our humour, lightly tossed throughout our lives, can do just that - keep the equilibrium as the inner sanctuaries are protected. I am able to stay steady when a lot of fairly harsh and constantly demanding situations arise with my own body and then managing the consequences. Whilst I have my own control panel on the thermostat stable, no matter what happens on the outside, even if everyone else has control panels that seem off, I can remain constant. We all know those days when everyone seems enraged, knarky, tearful or just all over the place, so if we can remain the calm in others' storms then everyone settles instead of more chaos escalating. As our own extremes in our own heating and water systems become balanced, then there becomes less emphasis on extremes within and outside of ourselves.

In order to serve and be there for another, we need willingly to be with our own sources of dis-ease. That way we are safe and honest about what a mess we also make of our relationships.

Life is not often marketed as events that are constantly giving us chances to get the hang of our own navigational system. In order to be any good at anything in life, including managing ourselves, we will endlessly be rather hopeless at initially using our own equipment.

Frank Muir, the comedian told a story of hearing that if you like a girl you nibbled her ear. At a very young age in his school he sidled up to his heart's desire at school and began to nibble her ear. Unfortunately she had earrings and he had an orthodontic brace. So, apparently, they got so locked together that the gardener had to put them in the wheelbarrow and run them to the local hospital.

On the day when we are just below our own lines of being ok or are just miserable, our thermostat requires us to become better at being kind and giving ourselves the kind of warmth, attention and gentle encouragement that we would to a friend. We need to get better at being intimate with ourselves, and not running into frothy entanglements that would create drama. Dramas that would in the past be a way of us distracting ourselves, and for just long enough to not feel whatever it was that our own clever system was trying to alert us to.

This same patient had been taught to deeply mistrust his own body so he was doing what I know so many of us do. We are also being taught to mistrust our own feedback mechanism. He would use people, places and events as a kind of mood altering activity which does work, but needs to be understood before our own systems start failing under the sheer heat of such constant activity. That constant activity is often keeping us hidden from what our real needs are.

So in my own case as another example: Before I had really learnt about my own energy I always doubted my sanity. Feeling very ill most of the time, and incredibly vulnerable with no one really understanding what was wrong with me and my life already taking very differing twists to my peers, it was so easy for me to come to the wrong conclusions about myself. I was so incredibly exposed in ways that the thermostat hates, from endless letters being written in rather pompous, disparaging ways about my body and symptoms, to forever being asked to strip and being examined by total strangers. Medics often appeared unaware that the semi naked person standing in front of them was alive, and not just a 'THING". I was also contending with handling the need for surgical emergencies which would suddenly make it clear why I was in such pain. My triple burner in part had so much to cope with. The medical world was a constantly bewildering place where I never felt safe. Medically my experiences constantly were all or nothing. The nothingness of no one helping me, at all, with how ill I was, or the need for sudden surgeries.

Before I was diagnosed with Ehlers-Danlos syndrome, I remember saying to one of the surgeons who had just operated on me, "It's very odd but I feel psychologically much more stable now with the plates that you have put in my spine."

His response startled me, as he was kind but ferocious.

"Young woman, I never want you to question your psychological stability again, as we were only saying in our meeting about you that if it wasn't for how stable you are psychologically, you never would have made it this far. We have never met anyone who has walked with such a bust up back. There has been nothing holding you upright for years physically."

I did receive and still do to this day treatments from Chinese Medical practitioners who weekly kept and keep me balanced on an energetic level.

I share real stories from my life and the lives of others as they are endless proof of what is possible for us all. No matter what life brings us, we can endlessly use it as a springboard for more integrated health, even if, actually in the actual process of transforming another layer of dis-ease. Living with a connective tissue disorder that affects, literally, every single function of my body gives me plenty of scope for this to be living proof of working with the laws of nature. When understood these natural laws, can be harvested to manage, handle and even transcend what challenges/opportunities that come to us. As I live with more vulnerabilities than the average and well person I need to cherish my own clever system of guards and thermostat control carefully.

I also live with another condition known as Postural Orthostatic Tachycardia Syndrome. Basically, whilst a normal body has experiences of a steady heart rate and blood pressure with differing changes in posture, mine is not at all steady. When sitting upright or altering my position, my blood pressure which runs too low anyway, will drop further whilst my heart rate will escalate as there will not be enough blood circulated back to my heart. Yet, with the investment of regular treatments, my triple burner, which is constantly having to be hyper-vigilant and yet relaxed, manages to keep working very effectively. I am not on the medications that other patients are on for this very debilitating condition. These drugs are known to interact with the drugs that other consultants want me on.

Am I completely through the other side with all that my childhood and this illness have challenged me with? No, again and again, of course not, as to the same extent that our literal heating systems need to be serviced, or our actual fires need to be stoked having been replenished with logs, there will always be a need for participation.

I will never get away from the cyclical nature of all things in my own systems and in my humanity. Our fire individually and collectively is powerful beyond measure and yet equally is fragile. It needs our continual and consistent input, as do our treasured relationships.

In the case of the previous patient, to master his own fire energy and functions he had to commit to learning all he could about what really works in liberating us internally, connecting us to abundant life. He had to go from intellectually getting what needed to happen to it becoming embodied. With his own earlier experiences faced, and acknowledging that his original survival tactics had kept him alive, he discovered that they were no longer working and in fact were backfiring horribly on him. He was going to need courage to allow himself to be joyful from a much deeper place which treatment helped him with hugely. Understanding that quick fixes cannot work, bar the emergencies, when of course we do need very quick solutions, therefore we need to be willing to embrace laying down a deeper foundation of self-awareness in our mind, body and spirit. Importantly, it was vital for him to understand that the quick fixes ultimately robbed him of understanding the brilliance of his own functioning that was able to keep setting him free from the tangled webs that his childhood had handed on to him. The lack of profound knowing would not produce the long term and sustainable energy/heat for his system to be in optimum vibrant health. Or, in the case of making fires that were to be sustained, he chose very differently who he could and could not be intimate with, and who would be safe for him to take time to unravel with. He needed to rekindle the embers that were actually still steady and burning within him. He also had to learn how to grieve and not just on an intellectual level. There was much in the still of night that he needed to gently allow himself to come to terms with that had affected his fire deeply. His relationship with himself needed to be expanded into.

There are many consequences for all of us of the huge, tectonic-like shifts that take place in our lives. Rarely does it not affect our connections with everyone around us. The hardest thing to come to terms with having listened to so many people's responses and had plenty of my own, are the total shifts in what was familiar in our friendships. Suddenly and often the fire just goes out in them.

By becoming ruthlessly honest with ourselves and much more consciously aware of our part in something painful that arises, particularly with our interactions with others, we are incredibly internally liberated, which in turn actually frees us up to not become bitter, cold and/or cut off. When we talk about the energetic interactions in what is called our Summer, our fire element, we slowly begin to see that nothing is isolated. So, in the case of friends that have seemingly cut us off, or the flames in our connection extinguishing, it helps a lot to genuinely and honestly look at our parts in what has happened. It is way too easy in our society at present to get away with making out that we are victims of others' behaviours, whereas the truth about the nature within us is that we are much more in charge of what happens than we initially think.

When our thermostat is on the blink or not working at its maximum, we can have a multitude of dilemmas and challenges going on all at once, whilst our bodies simply will not be keeping our temperature even on all the levels that we never necessarily think of. We can then simultaneously be finding it tricky to sustain loving and connected relationships. We will be slightly blowing hot and cold with our dear ones, giving off conflicting messages, withdrawing and being shut down whilst also seemingly inviting interactions. Blowing hot and cold is an excellent metaphor for when this aspect of our feedback system is struggling.

Often, when a person has too much shock or trauma in their younger lives, it is as if the thermostat has gone on the blink. I use that word blink literally, even though it is one of the English expressions and slang. I remember hearing a mechanic describing what was wrong with my father's car, "She has gone on the blink, sir, good and proper like."

"What on earth does that mean, Daddy, and why has that man described our car as 'she?' You do that, too?"

Daddy would always describe his cars as "she" and with great affection as he adored cars. In fact, when he was having great fun with us, which is a characteristic of the thermostat, he would demand in serious but playful tones when driving, "Darlings, lean forward quickly! Help out the great car as she roars forward! She needs our help!"

Our thermostat can bring a sense of warmth, spontaneous joy and laughter to all sorts of situations. It can bring about a sudden and needed burst of heat or fluid release, or sweat.

So, going on the blink is a brilliant expression for exactly what happens with the thermostat in our lives when it is asking for more balance and harmony. I sometimes think of the thermostat system and energy in our bodies as the sprinkler systems that all hotels and public places now have, with now the added luxury of under floor heating. If, a fire or smoke was detected, then, immediately the sprinkler system would work to put it out. Equally, the heating system can and is controlled by thermostats to regulate your body temperature and heating systems.

However, when your thermostat is caught up in a greater priority which involves your overall health and well-being, or, from a western perspective your immune system is being compromised, then the energy gets diverted.

My own thermostat energy has been masterful in protecting me over 35 anaesthetics, which pushes the body to extremes, as well as the healing that needs to take place for the surgeries in the first place. With the condition I have, I do not absorb anaesthetics well or at all in a so-called normal manner, so I have to be given much higher quantities of the very few drugs that my body will accept without going into more of a reactive and inflamed state, so the recovery is much more traumatic and problematic. The last few massive surgeries that I have had, I went into them on my knees on every level. Exhausted as I had not slept at all or properly for almost five years, and ten years before that with the increasing levels of pain, so my thermostat was already desperately on the blink.

On a spiritual level, though, as I would go through long nights awake and in huge levels of seemingly uncontrollable pains, I ended up having the experience that the thermostat can facilitate. It is understood that, as we evolve through the three sections of the thermostat, we can begin to have a deeper internal awareness of the integration between the three main philosophies of religion. Confucianism, Taoism and Buddhism begin to harmonise together within our own beings and very particularly in our actions and behaviour without us having necessarily even come across anything to do with either of these deeply integrated views about life. During my long nights when the only wise option open to me was to stop resisting what was my reality, I had to increasingly surrender to something far greater going on than it appeared in my wretched frenzy and misery. At a far deeper level than I had experienced before I was being strengthened in the receiving, processing and elimination functions. I struggled for some semblance of control over my own body's mechanisms, like sleep or bladder control. After spinal surgeries and the complications my syndrome shares, it is often also the bladder that will be hyper, so nights are problematic anyway. So, in my wanting access to some semblance of balance again, I was out of step with what my body needed. It had been through such extreme trauma on so many extended levels that it knew certainly better than I did what I needed. It seems so obvious that I would need rest and restorative sleep and yet actually what I needed even more was to make friends with another layer of my deeper connection to an internal light. The internal light or fire is inherent in us all, and it is one of our main facilities.

If I had not understood what my body was doing on so many occasions after I came around, I think that I honestly would have given up the ghost. What an incredible expression that is, as an aside, although in this case it is relevant and deliberate. Giving up the ghost is almost exactly what it feels like when your thermostat's energetic system is being diverted elsewhere.

In the America where I have had a lot of the procedures, they have warmed up blankets that they put on me as I come around, ice cold and in such shock.

The first line of defence seems as if it has gone, so to begin with, depending on how severe the trauma is, in the case of my surgeries I would feel incredibly shaky, tearful and anxious. On some occasions when I was back home needing huge amounts of support in all functioning of everyday things, I would be so punch drunk with my temperature control being seemingly totally on the blink, when it was actually busy putting out the equivalent of fires

196

and working hard on the healing processes. All of my responses to everything were slow, flat and lifeless as I struggled to come back to something that I remembered but no longer was able to self-generate internally. I was a full-fledged wax work of my former self, or ghost-like. I would have to have someone either in the room with me or actually lying with me holding my hand as I just went through being ice cold, weeping with an utter sense of being partially dead already. No amount of hot water bottles or blankets would reheat me. All the energy had gone to the source of the immediate priority. So, it is like your sprinkler system defending your home, in the case of a fire. Nothing else but the emergency matters.

Now, if this is a vivid enough picture of your thermostat, you can begin to imagine on an emotional, spirit/essence level with your connection to yourself and others how important this one aspect of your summer season and your own fire is.

Very often, and as a good example that you all may have noticed in others, when two people meet and there is an obvious spark between them, initially it can be very flirty and fun. However, quickly and almost before your very eyes, what appeared to be full of perhaps possibility turns into a mess of conflicting emotions. One or other, or both people, start blowing hot and cold as if neither of them has enough internal fire to sustain what seemed initially so full of spark.

I have had deep friendships with amazing women whose strengths and potential area for growth / strengthening / stretching was in their thermostats. In hindsight, I wish that I had known then what I have to come to understand about the fragilities/strengths of this energetic pattern. When they were interacting with the world, they were all very engaging, available and attentive. They were very shiny, as if the fire in the room came from them. I am sure that I never fully realised, though, that for them to sustain that level of warmth outwardly did not necessarily mean that they had it in themselves. So, it was almost like a false fire that they felt energetically propelled to give or be, in order to keep themselves internally stable. All the women could withdraw, or suddenly be bitchy, shut down or spark off without any warning. The fire within them would just suddenly die.

The point of this book is to keep sharing all the amazing ways in which there is truly a feedback mechanism going on all of the time, which is not on any level confined to verbal. We are so very much more than our present educational system is presently portraying. So, if we go back to seeing the thermostat as similar to the thermostat in our homes, we begin to get more of an idea of our own brilliance.

When our fire systems are in balance we have laughter and joy that spills out easily. Internally, when the fire is steady we can take ourselves very lightly - lightly tossed. In the next chapter, I introduce the next layer of our protection systems in our fire, summer season.

Unglamorous Tips For Glamorous Living
Or Tantalising Teasers

Spend time thinking about how much more vulnerable you or some of your friends might be. Think in terms of how some people go hot and cold in a nanosecond. Warm one moment, cut off the next. Do not judge, just observe.

To succeed in anything in life, it is vital to really begin to know yourself, then others as an automatic consequence.

Always and in all ways please keep asking yourself whether a state of dis-ease has its roots in your mind, body and spirit.

Use the time to be a friend to your own body, your mind and your spirit. Knowing that it is the marriage of this combination that becomes the greatest friend you will ever have. Think in terms of how your own thermostat runs in your relationships. Consider who you interact with in your world. Are you deliberately allowing consistent warmth to come through for those that are special to you? Are you being loving, kind and warm? Do you get up from your chair when your loved one arrives? Are you able to make others feel important?

Spend a few days while reading the chapters on the Fire about your heating and water systems in your own home and allow yourself to realise that you also have the same in your own clever and brilliantly orchestrated body. Once you can get the hang of your own thermostat, you can begin to read others and side-step the sometimes inevitable scalding that has to continue to be expelled until their or your control panel internally is altered.

Drugs: this is NOT to suggest you stop any, but it is an invitation to think through more what your own body is maybe telling you. Allow yourself to use drugs as knowledgeably as possible, not reneging on your authority over your body.

No drugs will ultimately alter what has not been fully understood in the first place; this is a huge and controversial subject but you will see already why I have come to understand that this is the case. With blood pressure issues look at what your own Fire, thermostat is telling you. So then alongside what your own practitioner/doctors are saying be willing to work with what the underlying issues may be. Always be willing to find out what the dis-ease is really telling you. Are you nutritionally deficient? Get hold of, for instance, an integrated functional medical practitioner or nutritionist.

Have in your own bookshelf (very old fashioned of me but I will always be trying to reduce the ways in which we all conduct our lives through electromagnetic fields which is NOT good for our systems.)

- Earl Mindell's 'Vitamin Bible'

Or

- 'Nutritional Solutions for 88 Conditions' by David Rowland.

Find Ways Of Allowing Joy And Laughter Into Your Life Regularly.

Watch, Read Or Do as a discipline for your Wellbeing and the health of your Thermostat

- Your Favourite Comedians
- Funny Films and / or Show
- Laughing Yoga
- 'Poems of Hope and Joy: I heard God laughing. Renderings of Hafiz' by Daniel Ladinsky.

Find out what works for you, not others, which then will mean that you can much more reliably be available and consistently for others.

I am also going to mention a fabulous Book called 'Talking With The Animals' By Patti Summers, An animal Whisperer. Our fire energy is often heartened literally and warmed by contact with the Animal Kingdom. So this is an enchanting book reminding us, of course, of what so many of us know with our relationships with our own animals.

Consider getting yourself an animal to look after if you are longing for a level of companionship that will require you to be consistent with feeding, watering and walking or whatever the animal needs. In return you will receive so often far more real life lessons of intimacy and safety than you would ever imagine (if having animals is new to you).

They do clearly communicate with us, so be open to what your own fire needs and wants from the animal kingdom.

The fire likes interactions with others so if you are too isolated, see what you could or would become a part of. What are your skills? A couple of friends of mine love washing up and volunteer to do just that in some charities. They humbly say that it is their time for them, whilst also it is serving others so it is a win, win. Both are men!

Lastly dancing is a great way to warm up your own FIRE ENERGY.

Summary of the Triple Burner/ thermostat chapter

Thermostat

The Triple Burner is associated with the Summer Season

The element is Fire
The colour is red
The sound is laughter
The odour is scorched
The emotion/energy is joy and radiance

The function of this organ is to allow for Balance and Harmony, opening up passages and irrigation. Regulation of fluids stems from it.

The associated functions/organs are: Small Intestine (Chapter 8)
Heart (Chapter 9)
Pericardium (Chapter 10)

A Balanced Summer provides the ability to:

- Give and receive love with appropriate degrees of emotional closeness
- Knowing how and when it is ok to open up or shut down to others
- Deciding how much to open up to others in all different forms of relationships

Behaviours that shows up when our fire is out of balance

Compulsively cheerful	to	miserable
Open and overly sociable	to	closed and isolated
Clowning	to	earnest
Vulnerable	to	over protected
Volatile	to	flat

Chapter 8

Discover your

Small intestine

Your internal committee and boardroom

Fire/ashes

The small intestine is the official in charge of receiving, being filled with transforming; the separator of the pure from the impure.

Our Fire internally and externally allows us the ability to give and receive love with appropriate degrees of emotional closeness. It helps us know how and when it is appropriate to have ourselves be open or shut to people. Like a control panel on our walls for our heating systems, we also have our own inside of us. The control panel helps us to know how much to open up to others in all different forms of relationships.

An attractive man walked in to my treatment room and almost immediately said, "A wild cat has just walked into my midst, stunning as hell and turned my world inside out and upside down. You see I am gay, and I have never fancied a woman. This one though, jeepers. She knows I am gay or at least has always assumed I was, and totally, never bisexual. She knows but will not accept that it is now only her that I want, which actually I respect as all my gay friends tell me I am off my rocker and cannot possibly, suddenly, be so turned on by a woman. They just do not get it and nor does she. In my bones and my soul I know that she is my soulmate. There won't be anyone else like her for me. It is totally beyond gender. Do you get that?"

I indicated to him that I did totally get what he was saying. In clinical practise and in another situation that I have been involved with since my early teens, I have witnessed many shifts in the expression of people's sexuality, as it is never an isolated expression.

"How on earth can I accept either that she will never trust me, therefore not become my wife, let alone be in a relationship with me, or that by taking this path which I completely want, that I must also lose all my friends? They are now ganging up against me. Presumably, they feel so threatened by this utter shift in me. Even now without her in my life something has happened that is so beyond my control that I have to go with it. Will you help me as I sense that the philosophy and ancient wisdom of the East will help me through this shock? It's clearly time for me to sack my present committee and serve all the directors notice."

Assuming nothing, I asked him about his last sentence before I responded. He replied, "Oh, well you see when I was very young my father helped me come to terms with my sexuality whilst my mother was totally freaked out, thinking that somehow she had failed me. She was also desperate to be a grandparent. My PA introduced me to the idea that I have a group of directors in my own mind, alongside a committee of either gaggling geese, as he used to call them, or serene swans, that are on my side in all matters. He used to teach me that, periodically, with life's events, we need to be willing to be ruthless if necessary and sack any committee members or directors that are not for me. He taught me how we all have voices in our heads, which are usually taken from our past or our parents, which do not necessarily serve us. So, we are forever on our own backs, which will not help us go forward and flourish in our lives. He was a firm believer in Jesus Christ and never lost his faith, even when his church rejected him totally when he stood by me. He knew that his faith had room enough for what seemed to be my path so he never shamed me. Whilst taking it totally on board with me when the outer "gaggling geese" began with their noise, when I came out at such an early age. He found another church that we all used to go to and were welcomed by. Anyway, I digress. Does that explain it?"

Yes, indeed it had. So, I then went on to say that yes, I did get what was going on and that yes, he would receive the support to negotiate what would happen in this, his largest transition so far on an integrated level.

At the end of this chapter you will find out what happens.

By becoming aware of the committee members that we have in our minds boardroom, we can always sack them all if they are not serving us, as this patient's father taught him. You can replace them with committee members that are actually on your side. That way, when the inevitable challenges do hit the fan, we at least can be semi-prepared to be in charge of our own boardroom. When we become aware of what our differing voices are saying, we can then go on to find ways of actually quieting our mind at our will. We can also master how we are being treated outwardly. For as sure as eggs are eggs, if we are allowing an internal bully to have a voice, then we will also have an outward one. (Experiment with this idea; as so many patients have begun to also find the correlation) The small intestine within our own system will be sorting continually the pure of our internal and external dialogue, for instance.

The twist to this writing is this: I want to show you that whilst it is fashionable to talk about our minds, to practise "mindfulness," it is important to know that I will always be referring to your energy.

What do I mean by that?

Our thoughts respond constantly to a feedback mechanism from what we do, what we eat, what our chemistry is, what the energy and life force was of our parents on our conception, and then lastly what consciousness we bring to mastering our minds, bodies and spirits. Actually, our mind is in every cell, as is our essence/life force. There is not this huge division, as if we were disembowelled and separated. Our energy is the fuel that propels us forward from

206

our entire being. Each and every single organ that we have in our body has an aspect of our spirit that is constantly evolving or is stuck, stagnant and causing us challenges. Of course, when we are getting our beings around a new concept associated with each and every facet of our lives, none of it will seem simple. However, with practise, the seemingly most complex of systems suddenly becomes simple. In the same way, at present dis-ease and ill health is not routinely associated with these concepts. If it is being taught, so many people are getting the idea that there is so much more wrong with them than even their own "gaggling geese" are saying. So many patients used to feel safe enough to instantly tell me how ashamed, guilty and overwhelmed they felt. Despite huge outward success they felt they were utter failures, the apparent stupidity of their decisions, choices, jobs or even their lives had an impact. So, many sessions early on in getting to know patients would literally begin with:

"What on earth is wrong with me? Why on earth can I JUST NOT GET IT?"

"I am just not learning this lesson."

"I MUST BE SO BRAIN DEAD. I keep having to relearn this lesson."

"Clearly, my life will be better once I HAVE LEARNED these lessons."

It was staggering to me to hear what almost sounded like a loss of innocence, the harshness and ruthless overpowering self-judgements. A very dear friend is always saying wisely, "You can't know what you don't know." Experiencing life can become as harsh or as responsive as our own inner dialogue. Not knowing needs to become an adventure that lifts and lights our inner fire, rather than battering it with our, and the world's, seemingly unforgiving energetic whipping.

When the organs are functioning well and in an integrated way, it becomes far easier to notice what we are doing and the feedback we receive. Literally, every single aspect of our own behaviours is returning to us like boomerangs. So, on the energetically damaging level, here is a list of behaviours that we all need to sort through and alter within ourselves:

- Bullying
- Shaming
- Blaming
- Scapegoating
- Humiliations
- Projections
- Jealousy
- Arrogance
- Snubbing
- Manipulations
- Scheming

Unfortunately these behaviours seem to be the norm where we participate in them, without having a clue. Even some self-help or Spiritual new age practices can, in of themselves, be all of the above.

So, the above that is so rife in our societies is indicative of what we are ingesting, having to sort our way through. We get so overwhelmed and yet are not being shown that we can actually affect our outer worlds by how we interact with our inner worlds.

Our control patterns overlay our heartbreaks and can turn into a very toxic, vicious cycle of endless drama. The small intestine, when it is not working properly, can have our behaviours be very two-faced, muddled as to what the pure for instance in our friendships is. We can participate in momentary power struggles with juicy gossip rather than being supportive or kind behind our real friends' backs. We can be cruel to our partners and yet seemingly gracious to others. We can give of our best aspects to the outside world only to share our most toxic with those who we claim to love.

Waking up to some of our own unpleasant behaviours, traits and patterns is enormously liberating. Sometimes, the reasons, stories and whys behind our acts become irrelevant as we switch our intention and focus to actually becoming different, catching our own toxic reactions and learn to act instead. When we truly begin to know that we are all in what I term the "soup of humanity" together, we can concentrate on sorting out our own behaviour that then affects the whole. (At the end of this chapter, I share Professor Hawkins quote that sums up this whole section stunningly.) It leads to a humbling sorting and literally, as we begin to take responsibility for our side of any and everything, our living, and our relationships, become not just clear but cleaner, as we begin to more consciously receive digested food and drink from our stomach and then can separate the fluids. It is mind-bending and will be overwhelming at first getting your head around these concepts. I was boggled at the beginning of my training and continue to practise mastering all of this valuable information daily. Falling flat on my face with endless mistakes but now not minding as the point to my daily living is now knowing that I can and do willingly practise the laws of nature. The laws of nature truly give me a continuous edge on a genetic disorder that could so easily be slaying me on numerous levels hourly.

It is fashionable now to master your mind, through some mindfulness or being present. Which is a fantastic step towards understanding the influence we have over ourselves, and our days. It is possible and even preferable to put our mind, body and spirit as one, then to also be inspired by getting our own feedback mechanisms. Once we learn to stop judging, bullying and shaming ourselves, we can neutrally assess what we are up to that needs sorting and changing. We can happily be not just the problem in our lives but, therefore, immediately the solution. No matter what is happening and whatever circumstances we find ourselves in, we can only ever master ourselves rather than the futile attempts at changing someone else. We can manage our daily lives by seeing, feeling and hearing the information that is being bombarded at us in overwhelming quantities in a totally different way through the magic of our own bodies, minds and spirits.

Goldie Hawn, the internationally acclaimed actress and conservationist, has a foundation that is responsible for teaching children all over the world about how their brain chemistry affects their bodies. Through the power of meditation, stilling their minds through the power of breath, Goldie Hawn is helping children to master the enormous levels of stress that they are experiencing.

Over 5000 years ago, the laws of nature were understood in a way that is deeply needed now, as we are separating ourselves from what is our very own life force. We are totally connected to nature inside and outside. It is as if we have so collectively poisoned ourselves that we have literally begun to "throw the baby out with the bathwater."

Life is so often presented as if we can master it in such a way as to not have a constant stream of challenges happening, a vision that would require constant attention, maintenance, and levelling. Surely, if we realised that, we would begin to also see that we have the ability to respond almost naturally and even unconsciously to the events, people places and things outside of us that we have no control.

If we understood that our body masterfully protects us, and continually, that if we willingly guided it in directions that adhered more to the natural cycles of our lives, then we would have less resistance. The more resistance we have internally in our organs, the more we automatically become magnets for the same on the outside of ourselves and with far less capacity to deal with the externals.

My mother had an expression that endlessly proves to be true but not quite as it seems: "No good deed ever goes unpunished." Thank God that the total unique balance of both of my parents' wisdom brought some clarity to this for me. I always associate this with the small intestine energy, as it is the mastering of our own internal committee that then allows us to have the wisdom and maturity of being able to assess what will happen when we do feel led to do a "good deed." Our father would take us aside and tell us that when we were in the positions to support, help or encourage others as we were taught from an early age to do, there would be times when the very person who had turned to us in their vulnerabilities would walk away without even so much as a thank-you. He explained that most people want no reminders of what it was like to be so out of control, vulnerable or having to be reliant on another person, so they would unconsciously get rid of you in their lives. Hence, no good deed goes unpunished. Of course, it is not always true and it is bringing a wacky family wisdom from my particular family. It reminds my incredibly thoughtful brother and I to continue being led by our natural gut instinct. Knowing often that others will have to interpret whatever we have felt led to do in those most vile of ways, yet still we go ahead putting on the equivalent of the rubber marigold gloves and share what is abundantly available to us all. He routinely is awoken in the night to talk someone down from wanting to kill themselves, for instance, and is endlessly kind, compassionate, and is truly, deeply involved with others' terrible misfortunes in very healthy ways. Yet, he will also take it in his stride when one of those people, having got back up again, will snub him or behave as if he is nothing to them. He knows it is their inner frailty that is still too raw and they are still too frightened to really be okay with how really fragile they were.

We have both gone through so much that we both know that strength comes from also accepting our frailties.

So, it is the job of the small intestine to sort out whether we need to prepare ourselves for helping when another fellow human is in trouble, but equally we sometimes have to prepare ourselves for the shifting sands that often fall when others cannot or will not sort through their stuff. There is always a timing that is typically beyond our individual knowing of when or even if another will awaken and shift their inner blocks. We can cherish our own fire properly so that we do not get blown off course of needing to be a generous person. We learn with maturity to give unconditionally to ourselves first and then others.

The absence of symptoms, issues or challenges in our lives is not vibrant, energetic life, or integrated health, there will always be just the next layer and opportunity to expand.

This is one of the main themes that I work with. Life is a continual process that asks us to show up, transform, and be transformed into more of who we really are on mind, body and spirit levels.

If, for whatever reasons, we are leading lives that seem unmanageable, miserable at times, or just downright confusing, or we are ill on varying levels, there are very few places that we can go to just be. Being with our own innate wisdom, to have time and space in this "busy being busy " world to discover what we are up to, to actually find that there is great and profound wisdom in each and every symptom that our precious lives are spitting out.

Traditional Integrated Chinese Medicine experiences, sees, hears and even smells all problems as potential that is ready for the next level of inner awakening. It is my privilege and honour to walk alongside remarkable people discovering how much stronger, braver and wiser they and their own clever feedback mechanisms are. Throughout my career, I have been asked to write about what takes place in the clinics I have had. Whilst I have walked alongside other's sorting, literally, the pure from the impure of their lives, we have together been a part of each other's journey. To stick to the intention of being a profoundly good practitioner as are those who have impacted my life dramatically for the better, I have had to be continually willing to keep being open to my own inner awakening. We never arrive and then pontificate to others from some seemingly elevated place. We may indeed be slightly higher up some mountain with a view that we can share with others, but that never makes us better. Real wisdom comes with the knowledge of how equal we really all are. A healthy small intestine with healthy knowledge of our own inner committee members shows us truly how interconnected we are.

So, back to our story, in this chapter there is just the one example of the shifts that in part can take place around a small intestine energetic imbalance. May I stress here that the actual differing states of how we are experiencing our sexualities is not a matter of moral judgement and is not muddied with harsh and inflamed opinions. Always, and in all ways, we are assessing the energy states of each and every organ as a whole, interconnected on all levels.

The patient who had come to me for support whilst he faced what amounted to the deepest layer of integrated spiritual (his own spirit) crisis that he had had so far, went on to indeed live "happily ever after" with his bride of his soul's choice, but not before going through some incredibly brave, humbling to witness, transitions.

He dug deep into his own behaviour before this woman had walked in and even begun to see that he had called her out of his own desire for real and lasting change to take place. He had begun to recognise that he was often being "murky" (his words) in most of his relationships; he often opted for how he termed the "murkier and nastier" aspects of expressing his sexuality which he had increasingly realised was so removed from loving another human being and building up a safe and lasting relationship. He also realised that he had never really, consciously, practiced intimacy and all that it entails. Once he shared the most powerful of dreams that was alerting him to his own actions and how much of a price he was paying, he knew almost overnight that he did not want to continue behaving any longer in the same split ways. The words he used to me were, "Overnight and almost literally the two sides of my life met. My behaviour on the one hand was actively operating from my faith and then on the other hand I had stepped away from my faith. Without even realising it I was living a split life, when in fact interacting with others outside the church that I had continued to be a part of. It was as though I was two different people: one that could be trusted and was able to be consistent with others, if superficially, and then another aspect of me, when any form of closeness came near me, destroyed it. I was then this callous, even cruel and cold, detached man that was not trustworthy. In fact, I now think that the real reason why my friends have all walked away from me was because I never really let them see the 'me' that I am far more comfortable with, and who I TRUST more. The shift in the expression of my sexuality was not really why they all walked away. It was just another sense of betrayal on my part - betrayal of being so false with them. My sudden expression of wholehearted passion and connection with another human being was what really shook them. It obviously made them realise how shallow I had been with them. Her appearance in my life had made the two aspects of my behaviour collide, making it impossible for me not to begin to be congruent."

This patient took a year to initially come to terms with such a vast shift in his whole orientation, whilst becoming a trusted friend to this woman. Only in the second year of knowing him did she begin to allow herself to fall in love and be willing to contemplate being with him.

Unglamorous solutions to glamorous living and tantalizing teasers

On the most basic of levels, start sitting down to eat in deliberately peaceful circumstances. Turn off noise around you and be still in your own "juices," literally ingesting more consciously. Start with one meal per week when you make it a loving and sincere gesture of discipline to yourself and your well-being. Sort out how to make it a "pure" occasion, away from clutter and distraction. Clear away the entire muddle from the table for instance. Clean out, symbolically, your fridge, your cupboards, your cooker. Prepare as if you were going to make a guest feel really welcomed – but do it for yourself instead.

Check out regularly who is on your own internal committee. Are you in charge of them or are they insidiously in charge of you? Have you really still got a voice from some bully or relation from the past ruling your actions from a position of power that you still give them by allowing them space in your being?

Spend time evaluating who you would like in your own board room. Put people who you admire, want one day to be similar to with some of their actions, for instance, or friends you love who you know love you unconditionally. It is your board room so be clear about sorting out who you really want, and who will be on your side, as you commit to living an integrated and passionately engaged life.

Allow yourself to be ruthlessly honest and watch if you are behaving in a two faced way. Are you being nice to people one moment and then being 'shitty' about them behind their back?.

Are you a gossip with no clear idea of how toxic your own active participation is?

Do you mind if you are someone that is unsafe and untrustworthy?

What are you prepared to do about your own actions if you recognise that you are neither?

Both of which I believe are something that we all can improve upon, all of the time, as our own relationship with ourselves becomes something more honest.

Listen and hear what our own life and actions are telling us.

Watch out for some of the following symptoms that may indicate that your small intestine is not happy: abdominal pain, scanty dark urine, burning pain on urination, severe mental restlessness, ulcers in your mouth, a twisting pain going around to your back.

Practise listening to one another and then be examples of really hearing. If we were at a point yet where we could listen to the next generations in ways that really relieved them of the stress in their young lives, their future would look brighter than it seems to be at present. Let it begin with you and listen whilst hearing yourself first, then others. Be a loving witness to your own voice, inner and outer; this concept in practice, in and of itself, would create a different world immediately.

Politeness is the greatest tool in your toolbox.

It can neutralise and deactivate the energy of most things, even if already in an inflammatory situation. However, it is necessary for us to find a degree of sincerity in having manners otherwise it is just another form of control and hiding behind a mask.

There was a very funny series of sketch's that showed a couple being verbally polite yet using so much aggression in their tone of voices that it showed through humour how rigidly controlled even manners can become.

Boomerang.

Think boomerang or if you are auditory start listening to the sound of the tone and noise of your own voice. If we fully take on board that every single thing we think, say and do are like boomerangs coming back at us then we do begin to take very different steps to change our relationship with ourselves and with our world.

Take on board that sometimes when you have a stiff neck and literally cannot turn it from side to side it may well be that you have got in to a muddle or polluted waters with some thing or an interaction concerning your sorting facility. You may just be having trouble sorting out what is what. The energy lines for your small intestine go through your neck. Be kind and gentle with these ideas and concepts though, as you may well also have had to crick your neck to prevent yourself from having something fall on you. Discern what is happening to you as your own body talks to you. Follow your own increasing sense of empowerment.

Look up 'Mindup', from Goldie Hawn's foundation, to learn about the incredible work she and her team are doing for our next generations. She is passionate about helping the children learn more about self-empowerment, breathing, meditation and their brain chemistry.

'Choose' and 'sort out' your life with a healthy small intestine. Once again, I recommend buying or finding in your library 'Clever Guts' by Dr Michael Mosley.

Lastly, decide consciously, at what energetic vibration do you want to live at, as purely as is possible or with muddle, that does constantly affect others. Knowing, humbly, that even with the commitment to live as purely as is possible, it will mean that we ourselves come across another layer of our own internal muddle, let alone the world's. With a healthy functioning Fire season within, we will always be able to laugh at ourselves, lightly tossed though, as in the previous chapter. According to the data that we are literally operating from, some of which is actually redundant to us, we will grow through layer after layer of sorting.

- 1 individual, vibrating and living to the energy of optimism and willingness to be non-judgmental of others, will counterbalance the negativity of 90,000 individuals who calibrate at the lower weakening levels.

- 1 individual, vibrating to pure love and reverence for all of life, counterbalances the negativity of 750,000 individuals who calibrate at the lower weakening levels.

- 1 individual, vibrating to illumination, bliss and infinite peace, counterbalances the negativity of 10 million people - (there are 22 such sages alive at the time of this writing)

- 1 individual, vibrating to grace, pure spirit beyond body loving complete oneness, counterbalances the negativity of 70 million - (approximately 10 alive at the time of this writing)

Summary of the Small Intestine chapter

Small intestine

The small intestine is associated with the Summer Season

The element is Fire
The colour is red
The sound is laughter
The odour is scorched
The emotion/energy is joy and radiance

The function of this organ is the separator of pure from the impure

The associated functions/organs are:
Triple burner/Thermostat (Chapter 7)
Heart (Chapter 9)
Pericardium (Chapter 10)

A balanced Summer provides the ability to

- Give and receive love with appropriate degrees of emotional closeness

- Knowing how and when it is ok to open up or shut down to others

- Deciding how much to open up to others in all different forms of relationships]

Behaviours that shows up when our fire is out of balance

Compulsively cheerful	to	miserable
Open and overly sociable	to	closed and isolated
Clowning	to	earnest
Vulnerable	to	over protected
Volatile	to	flat

Chapter 9

Discover your

Heart

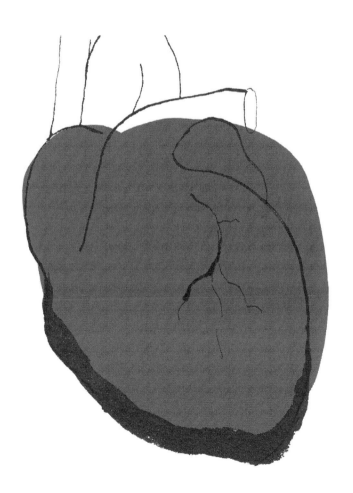

"Spiritual Spinning" or "Topping and Tailing"

The Heart holds the office of Lord and Sovereign.

Discover the functions of your Heart.

I was taught how to be a very effective spiritual spinner, topping and tailing my emotional states. I really bought for ages the idea that there are negative and positive emotions, when in actuality, in the world of nature and energy, endless opposing states and frequencies co-exist. So, no emotional state is good, bad, negative or positive. However, with the majority of us needing to fit in and be approved of, we plaster or do some form of topping and tailing our real emotional responses to the realities of our lives. We learn from such an early stage that our real internal responses to external stimuli are considered to be wrong. Simply put: by not knowing how to change gears energetically/emotionally, we fudge part of the very vital sat navigation system that is in us.

Real, vibrant energetic health gives us as an almost automatic response to life. So, when we are not using the wisdom of our own feedback mechanisms, we respond to our pains, emotional and physical, through a lens of 'Topping' the surface of the pain, avoiding the life-affirming experience of feeling all the emotions involved and are then convinced that we have "dealt with" or "controlled" the response, we have 'Tailed' it. 'Topping and Tailing', rather than developing more and more self-knowledge, keeps our organs from developing energetically. If we were taking our cars into dirty, cluttered car washes, our cars would come out scratched, and dirtier, costing us far more than we intended.

By not being comfortable with all the emotions and keeping them in a balanced state, we then find ourselves overreacting to all sorts of outside stimuli, which then has us living in very reactive states. We then react to what is going on internally within us and accumulate clogged up states; this taints our ability to respond to what is actually being presented to us. This, in turn, costs us and of course others much more than we intended. So, if our heart energy is being blocked up by layers of hurts, unexpressed emotions and responses, then it is tricky to have our very essence expressed radiantly. When our guards have been crushed with too many shocks or traumas (physical, mental or spiritual), we are acutely and chronically vulnerable. The king or queen within us, i.e., the Heart, cannot govern the internal or external domains in our lives.

Nature is about balance, but in ways that are separate from sentiments or belief systems that are attached like the stickiest of glue to us. Our heart, in its great energetic wisdom and when allowed to operate at its optimum, is humbly serving the whole of its energetic kingdom - our body. With the right support from the functioning other Fire systems, the heart gets on with governing appropriately and does not get bogged down with more than delegating in a detached way.

It took time for me to see how much trouble I was landing my heart in by my spiritual spinning and topping and tailing. I even had an overlay of very respectably considered qualifications that merely embedded behaviour that I know now, for sure, was not actually supporting the very people I was trained to support.

I had to unravel my own personal energetic blocks and defended states that my initial nine years of training was taking on board in layers:

I could not see   in the ways that I thought

I could not hear   in the ways that I understood

| I could not feel | in the ways that I sensed |
| I knew nothing | in the ways that I was educated to believe. |

In Chinese medicine, the common teaching is that all of life began with "phlegm." Within that "phlegm' is the inbuilt matrix for us to become what we are already. Additionally, mastering ourselves is having the "veils of illusion" burnt away "layer by layer."

So, even though you may well notice all the seeming contradictions in what our being is about, you will begin to see, hear, feel and know the comfort, hope and energy in all things. A sense of happiness and clarity are found in the middle of the contradictions, in the centre of all conflicting emotions that impact us around people, places and things. Our heart governs with an equilibrium that allows us to settle within, in spite of, and then even with the constant paradox of all of life, hence giving us a sense of emotional stability within the flow of all of our emotional responses in the constant changing ebbs and flows of life.

All of life is a bit like a seesaw, or even similar to the game of snakes and ladders. Once we are switched on to the purpose of our emotional and energetic states, we are quicker at understanding the language of our own clever, integrated and ever-changing states of health within our bodies.

One of my themes as a practitioner is that no matter what is happening, our body, mind and spirit knows exactly what it is up to. We are trained to see potential in all problems; in fact, we are trained to see the person as a whole, not as a series of issues, diagnoses, labels and findings. A very wise ruler, King or Queen, within has the insight to see beyond what is initially being presented to them in the inner sanctuary when the differing layers of security has filtered through all the happenings of the days. So, as good rulers, ideally our focus was and is never on problems, issues and then differing labels that then seemingly never alter.

Imagine going from hearing yourself participate in conversations like the first set of examples listed below to the last set of examples:

"Oh, you know she has so many issues."

"He is basically pretty messed up."

"They are just so negative. I can't handle them."

We now have so many ways of just throwing in the towel and basically being rather disparaging around those of us who, in our opinion, do not "cut the mustard" or are "a few sandwiches short of the picnic."

"Weird."

"Ugh, so many problems."

It is all said with the crazy notion that life does not come with, plenty of scope for experiences. We are not trained to automatically respond with our own vibrant energetic health to that of someone else's with statements such as:

- "Wow, I met someone today who was so inspiring with how they deal with a lot that is going on their plate all at once."

- "He has had some incredibly tough, mind-bending and energetically traumatic situations that leave me full of respect and wondering how I can be supportive."

- "I feel so challenged around this person as it appears they are not yet moving and shaking in their own resources. Mind you, I still have a long way to go before I can really claim that I have everything together."

Great rulers stay out of any inflammatory remarks about others as they know the influence they have and then equally that any inflamed actions are magnified by their every action.

Our hearts hold what we call the "shen", which is the energy of the heart. So, without knowing it, huge amounts of people are wandering around with what is known as "Shen Disturbance." It is as if they are not at home any longer. The sparkle in their eyes has gone. Even people who are able to be funny and sometimes even considered to be the "life of the party" are actually flat inside and without the real radiance that our hearts need to truly mature, or to know joy that does not need to consume and burn us. When our hearts are not energetically aligned with our real desires and needs, we can be compulsively cheerful, for instance, giving the impression of being in states of joy when, in fact, the opposite is true; that, in turn, means that the wrong signals are given off in that person's life force so their needs are never met.

I had a very dear patient who had had 3 heart attacks, six stents living alongside Arteriosclerosis for many years. His profession was one where he fronted up very publicly high profile hospitality. His heart, gifts and unique skills were highly sought after in a business sense as he had the skills to bring others together, to lead from the front, to assess in 180 degree ways the needs of large busy restaurants and hotels so that they hummed in a professional yet properly entertaining ways. He was entrusted to welcome and appropriately look after very high ranking members of differing societies from politicians to Royalty. Actually, though, what was at the root of his heart condition was a combination of differing factors that all linked up together to create the perfect storm for his body, physically, later on in his life. Being un-diagnosed early with what research has shown may well have proved his heart valves not fully opening at birth, he has courageously lived the life of two distinctly different and almost opposing personalities.

Throughout my patient's life, he had always known that something was not the same for him as others in his interactions with people. He lived with a constant sense of bewilderment and huge levels of frustration, never quite fulfilling the deepest yearnings of his own precious heart. His real hopes, dreams and expectations of life always seemed elusive. Later on in his life, he was diagnosed as being on the Autistic spectrum with a condition known as Pathological Demand Avoidance, which is now connected in some areas of expertise as being directly related to the physical functions of the heart, as well as the small and large intestines. So, he had had to contend with a chemical soup of extreme and high levels of anxiety, always snapping at his "shen." In the wiring of his functioning, there were levels of stress and strain that were not easily detected, of needing to have levels of control of the outside, to be in control, in turn, of the inside chemical soup.

Life has ways of layering events on that we do manage to transcend and that are certainly possible to do so far more than we are led to believe, or that become contributing factors to our own beings drowning in life.

My patient was not able to directly tell me anything relevant to what had been happening or share any insights or layers that had made up his life. He kept our sessions light, controlled, and well-orchestrated on a very sincere but entirely superficial level. He was charismatic, charming and seemingly very sparkly. However, when I read all the other ways that we are trained to see, to hear, to touch and to experience, a very different story was emerging. He was close to having another heart attack, massive this time, that I had no doubt was going to be the last. He was suffering from terrible leg and lower back pains which all proved to be more of the arteries blocking up. He was deeply troubled and unhappy in his marriage but totally unaware of his own needs as an overlay of continuous, internally reactive rage kept him in a mist of misery. I also discovered that his mother had been Alcoholic with his father coping with it by gardening, which he had internalised as a means to copy in his own frustrations. Going to work was his equivalent of his father's gardening. We coined his rage that I brought out into conversation his "killing machine," as it was a priority to begin to change as soon as was possible, but not before I had fully grasped what was actually happening so that I could direct treatments and help him.

Very tellingly, for the energy of the heart, an extremely traumatic event had happened in his childhood that came out as I treated his Fire, which he had not known was relevant to his heart or subsequent bottling of all of his emotional responses. As a relatively small boy learning to box, he had just won a championship against another boy. The following day in assembly, the whole school was told that the other boy had died.

As a direct result, and on a deep energetic level way beyond words which, with the autism are not easy to access anyway, he had from then on always repressed any external guarding or protecting of his own domain. The power of his own punch literally seemed, to him, to be responsible for another person's loss of life. In fact, we will never know the truth or real facts of this traumatic event. What I knew, though, as a practitioner, was to do everything within my capacity to restore his Shen as the overlay of constantly not trusting his own "punch," his own security system was in part playing a dangerous role in the very dangerous precipice he was standing on.

The adrenalised state needed to counteract the anxiety, bordering on terror, was so extreme with his condition that it was impossible for his heart to be intimate or to be present in ways that others would expect or want. To be sincerely superficial and, in his case, magically so, was so alluring to his workplace that no one understood the extreme strain that he was under. His wife, at the time of his heart beginning to show outwardly the strain of his particular lifetime's challenge, called him "the suit." It would have been impossible for her not to feel as if his work came before all else and that once "the suit" was off, after his work shifts, that there was nothing left for her. She would have witnessed how breathtakingly sparkly, seemingly gregarious, available and even deliciously flirtatious with life itself, he was while he was at work, only to then close down and be on occasion leadened when she wanted to be a part of that party sparkle that he was able to bring continuously to his work.

In the light of the Fire, summer season he was able to "fire up" for his work but not within his relationships. His work brought about a framework that allowed for some levels of familiarity that then provided security and containment, so that his system could have relaxed a little. All while though, while entertaining and looking after so many people, his own heart was suffering, until his whole system, but very particularly his heart, could not go on functioning safely.

We now know that in most levels of autism, the severe allergic responses to certain foods means that the intestinal tracts are always brewing up a fermenting level of toxicity that means that the body is being pushed into a highly inflamed state. That inflamed state has to be counteracted. Sugar is so often craved by autistic people as the lack of absorption of minerals and vitamins means that there is not the constant flow of energy to fuel a brain that does not have the same wiring as others.

Imagine the minute heating systems that cars have in their windscreens to defrost ice on the windows. In some cases, the heating system has breaks so the job of de-icing is not able to take place properly. Hence, there is an inability for some autistic individuals to have intimate relationships in the ways that they would like. One small child described her Pathological Demand Avoidance as like living with two entities, one a monster that never did what she wanted and was constantly fighting with the other aspect, a malfunctioning robot inside of her.

So, on the outside, my patient's life was full of activity and stimulation from his work life, which appeared to be very joy-fueled and with masses of laughter. Yet, on the inside his summer season was "scorched," flat, struggling with heartbreak and not understanding why he was not able to attain the types of relationships he really longed for. There was a total mismatch between his inside and outside. He had such a rich internal life of extraordinary passion for his children. The waters actually ran so deep within him yet generally people around him did not appear to realise who he was or what he struggled with. Much later on in treatment he was able to begin to understand more of the mismatches that went on for him. He began to identify how many relationships he had had where he was unable to be what others expected of him. Whilst he craved more interactions with others, he also had mechanisms within him that would have appeared to be pushing them away and not wanting to be involved. It was not that he did not want to be involved, but rather that his inner functioning was so fragile that he constantly had to protect himself as a constant priority and focus, which left very little room for anything outside of himself.

He had not been able to understand why his relationships did not seem to work for him, very often being attracted to Alcoholic women; their unavailability would have reflected back to him his inability to be able to connect to himself, let alone others. Equally his mother's Alcoholism that had affected him so much was unresolved within him. He had needed to be very personally self-focused, trying to keep himself safe and contained whilst the world had often seemed way too confusing for his particular internal kingdom to cope with. There are forms of autism that can often come across as similar to a diagnosis of Narcissism. Yet, the makeup of these two labels is very different. With gentle, kind, consistent support this particular patient was able to form a few friendships that remain in his life today, which is new for him, as they are able to be deeper than ever before. He did have another heart attack whilst he was learning a completely new way of eating and being, but it proved to be a minor one.

In his retirement, he was able to find ways of comfortably living with his conditions. His lifestyle had radically altered and he lived with what his heart needs, finding ways of keeping his fire settled yet gently stimulated. In his own words, he found a contentment, an acceptance of his autism and his heart condition. Instead of doing things that cause him maximum stress, he now will see whether he can handle something first.

By topping and tailing our emotions, e-motions, we also block our energy, our sense of aliveness, which keeps us on the defensive. This makes us often only aware of our perspective which again blocks the very things we crave to be and to receive. There are often examples of how the heart is not responding well to its job in the articles in newspapers all over the world. Reporters will write that the offending person sneared or smirked as if relishing in the harm they had done to another person in some crime committed. However, often this is simply not a correct energetic assessment of what is happening, as it is often the heart energy being so vulnerable that it is totally overwhelmed in shock. This is not to condone the behaviours that we witness; however, true freedom comes from realizing what really is going on, rather than our own superficial assessments that are often reactive.

Comedians will be able to vacillate laughter, merriment and even joy to vast audiences and yet, once the curtains are down, they often cannot retain anywhere near that for themselves or their spouses.

Whiskey is the drink of the heart; it fires a depleted heart without the drinker knowing. On receiving terrible news, shockingly to those who do not understand, and to the acute embarrassment of those who simply cannot help themselves, a person can find themselves laughing at what has been said?

When the heart is not in balance, the fire within can suddenly get out of control, almost superficially and become a burst of a flame to then die suddenly as the first impact has gone.

The Queen of England is an incredible example of a very healthy monarch. Our Sovereign has continued to reign for over sixty years through all sorts of profound events, as energetically intact as almost no other for that length of time. On the outside, there will always be judgments, particularly around her handling of the death of Princess Diana. Genuinely, she thought her first priority was to keep her grandchildren safe, to remain with them and yet almost certainly she may not have known how to be with their grief in them. Her response to the nation showed how ill-equipped she initially felt with such a devastating shock to the world in the death of the Princess.

Briefly here I will put a slightly differing take on the outpouring of grief that so many to this day do not understand. The Princess energetically represented an evolving opening to emotional and eventually mental health that the world is craving now. By the sudden loss of her under shocking circumstances, the nation's heart was broken, to ultimately and hopefully become stronger. Princess Diana had had the capacity to connect deeply to the sick, the burdened, to all those normally rejected in our societies. So, on a deeply important and energetic level she represented, as the young royals now, some vital governing of our own heart's capacity, which included those aspects of ourselves that cause us the most heartache and yet the vital clues to how to live more abundantly and with a simple joy unconditionally. However, from the vibrant health of what a Sovereign does, the Queen did respond to the advice around her in time to bring a grieving nation together. She is a remarkable example of what is possible within all of us. Our heart will serve us to its last heartbeat, literally, and never has a moment off as it continues to pump blood and oxygen to every corner of our own energetic systems. As fairly and as justly as its neutral capacity, it pumps and beats in rhythm 24 hours a day, seven days a week.

A love which the heart knows, not intellectually but viscerally, is what automatically flows from a balanced heart. What we want, though, is what we have to become. The natural cycles of life actually have a way of showing us. The heart dictates to us to be the love that we so often want from others. So much of life shows us that in order to be what it is that we identify we want, we need to become it for ourselves.

A PERSONAL STORY

My spiritual spinning was so effective that it allowed me to bypass all sorts of grieving, frustrations and appropriate emotional responses to the medical challenges and dramas that I was always, sooner or later, returning to. My spiritual spinning, as I realised it was, was going into overdrive every time painful emotions were coming up around the powerlessness of my medical condition, which I would judge as being wrong and bypass as quickly as possible. I became adept at bypassing, avoiding and diverting my own and others' attention, replacing the accumulating losses. It was not enough that with other areas of my life I was in fact beginning to be very comfortable with my own anger, the purpose and use of it, and my sadness around many things for instance. Whilst I was learning all sorts of tools to "deal" with my emotions, the words "resolving" or "recovering" never came up with the "dealing" of them. Only afterwards did I realize that feelings do not require to be "dealt " with; they need to be felt to their often unfathomable bottoms to then become something totally the opposite of whatever we are experiencing.

However, when it came to the medical condition that I had been born with, I was experiencing increasing layers of shock and not knowing at all how much trouble was brewing for me, medically. Quickly I began to learn though how to manage the pain that was to take years yet to understand or be diagnosed properly. Partly by making sure that I dealt with any grudges, or making sure that I was not harbouring any judgments. I learned and ended up teaching the importance of keeping the energy clear in my own body. If I did not do this I would have at least 50% more tension, which then in and of itself made the pain worse. I had never really been allowed to have any of the appropriate emotional responses to my own particular reality, let alone the shocks involved. As such hard struggles for just the basics that so many people take for granted was constantly denied, I, too, denied my needs. I looked well and able bodied but mostly was ill in ways that I now realise would have tipped huge amounts of people into a permanently switched off state.

Unbeknownst to me, I had swallowed completely the reflections I had experienced over and over again from Western and alternative medical practitioners, even from my own profession. The collective reflection I got was one of almost no compassion, kindness, consideration or encouragement on any level to do what would have been appropriate. No one had ever asked me how I was doing, or feeling, until the day arrived when some humanity sat in front of me. A wonderful practitioner and director of one of the colleges I was at, was giving me some support. She asked me a question about my medical situation. I answered it. When I looked up I was struck by tears rolling down her eyes as she said, "I am so sorry, Catherine. It's painful to see how much you have had to go through alone. How have you managed to stay essentially intact?"

That moment alone might have been what started the iceberg melting. I had been seen in my own inner sanctuary and fed back the vital humanity of being really okay with this condition.

So, at a time when I needed myself the most and I had to have the next surgical procedure, I was stuck. I did not have a clue that all the spiritual spinning of huge gratitude for instance was not, in fact, serving me. Giving my life the whole time what I call top spins, as if I was playing tennis, had been contributing to now an iceberg within me that had started melting and would not be ignored any longer. So, as I was told I needed to have emergency surgery again, that there was not a choice, I knew that I would not consent to more surgery.

The loss of my bladder and bowel function, use of my legs and spinal functioning was on the line, putting huge strain on my heart and all its respective functioning. The intracranial pressure not being stable, a worsening condition that I have had, was massively beginning to affect me in ways that none of us understood yet.

To my slight surprise, I just knew that I was not able to go ahead and have more surgery. It bemused me as, after all, I had had so much already – so, what on earth was my problem? I was catapulted head first into a massive, blinding depression that meant that I no longer wanted to live, let alone face another huge procedure. I was truly stuck not trusting myself to find the next solution; in fact, I was not interested or motivated to do so. Through a very long night, I diagnosed myself and realised that I was hitting a wall of grief and heartbreak that had suddenly started crumbling inside me.

By spiritually spinning, topping and tailing, I had persuaded myself and others that I only felt extreme gratitude for the privilege of still being able to be alive, to walk. I was grateful for the incredible surgeon and his team that had already done an amazing and extraordinary job with me.

One procedure was 20 hours long, requiring the co-ordination of three surgical teams. It was so easy to focus on how fortunate I was. I had even come through a stroke and a couple of cancer diagnoses requiring still more surgeries. So, I had had this "story " in my own head running for so long that it hadn't occurred to me to also face what my life's journey had actually meant - the cost on me, my body, my bank account, my career, my friendships, love and family life.

Wanting approval or, actually, in my case, not wanting another beating of verbal abuse from various family members, or a world that simply did not understand the extremes of medical challenges that I faced daily; I had become motivated to quickly access what the world required to be acceptable. The world loves what is now so tragically popular: "a positive person," "a positive spin." So, no wonder, at last, my own iceberg of grief was melting and crumbling.

The body will never ever carry for us our inability to keeping facing the truth, whole truth, and nothing but the Truth "Me Lord." It's interesting that the heart is always with its three other counterparts, the small intestine, the triple burner-thermostat and the pericardium, aligning itself with our integrated truths.

I was well and truly heartbroken, shattered by so much shock and on so many levels. My heart needed to be mended by witnessing unconditionally, deeply, and intimately what I had gone through. When that happened over a three-day period, with exceptional support and love, my emphatic "no" to more life-saving surgery turned into a "yes."

By becoming aware of and in tune with what our emotions are telling us, we can keep our hearts functioning at their optimum - filtering information all of the time. The aim is to disentangle ourselves from the pains of the past, present or even the projected future, so that our feelings become a true barometer to guide us. A lot of the time we are triggered by others' perspectives. Then, based on how others have treated us, we form sometimes dangerous misconceptions of ourselves.

The heart has a way in real health of observing from a guarded place what is real and what is not. Imagine the Queen of England in her own private study, surveying all the information in her red dispatch boxes. Whilst she is safe and protected, it is easier for her to wisely assess what she is reading through, remaining as detached as service to our nation requires. It would not work for any of us if she was a Queen who was always reacting and not knowing how to act wisely. In recent history, there are those who think that she mishandled some emotional tight ropes that she was on. However, her versatility in self-correcting with the protection of her own energetic functions has served well for a long time.

Unglamorous Tips for Glamorous Living Or Tantalising Teasers

When massive trauma of a violent, sexual or emotional nature takes place, often the heart dissociates itself with the event. We can go numb. However, when an immediate way of coping then sticks, it blocks our intimacy with others. So, if you know that you are not able to be as intimate as you would like with another, it is worth having some treatments with a very trusted practitioner of integrated medicine or going to a counsellor to see if some real events have gotten stuck but which you are not consciously remembering.

Become aware of exercise around the heart functioning. For instance, running can strain and weaken the circulatory system. We tend nowadays to buy the idea that we can do whatever we make up our minds to do, but we sometimes lack real understanding of what is energetic supportive to our whole being. Allow yourself the time to find out what your true intentions are with exercise, as we stress our bodies so massively when in fact we are "running" from something.

Check out how much time you feel able to really give to the precious children, God-children, nieces or nephews that you have. Are you imposing on them your unresolved issues or are you continually allowing them the consistent closeness, love and warmth that nourishes relationships? Are you too busy being busy? Are you able to make them or your partner feel as if they are the most important person in your world? Do you regularly tell your loved ones that they are precious and that you love them?

Create regular ways of celebrating how joyful life can be.

Put regularly times in the diary, no matter what your budgets are, or no matter what age to you are, to play - to have music, dance and adventure in your days.

Always have some things to look forward to that lift your heart.

Watch out how protected you are in your interactions. Are you allowing intimacies to grow and be nurtured in your life?

Practise watching how well your own heart is governing your own life. Regularly spend time alone and being still, practising just breathing fully and savouring how you really are. Then, respond to the information that will come up as you just sit with yourself. Find a way of resting and refuelling yourself regularly. For example, a woman in charge of a massive corporation used to daily ring her secretary to tell her to stop all calls until further notice. She would then sit down in a comfortable chair in her office with some heavy keys that were belonging to all the important doors, cupboards, etc., in the whole office block. She would place them in such a way that as she just sat switching off her mind and focused on her breath she would almost fall asleep. As she was just falling asleep the keys would drop to the floor bringing her fully back to being alert once again and refreshed. It usually took about twenty minutes before she would then resume her workload. Find your own way and keep it up for the well-being of your own heart.

Bring ritual into your life. Find ways that suit your own passions. If it is regularly listening to wonderful music, for example, then keep to the commitments to do that.

Learn all that you can, step by step, about what really nourishes your heart mentally, physically and spiritually. Nothing has to be overwhelming, though, so make it fun and do small steps at a time. Just watch what you do around all the contradictions that are out there around food, for instance. Find your own way, allowing your own heart's wisdom, the time, love and warmth through your own intention to find its way.

Watch out for how damaging forms of compulsive action are. Instead, begin to distinguish between spontaneous action, which is when the Fire energy can safely let go of joy, or to compulsive energy, which hardly works.

Friendships are important to the heart. Be as wise with your own treasured friendships as your heart is to the governing of your own kingdom.

Notice how overstrained you can become around eating, drinking, entertaining and being around others. Stop and assess how you are with others. Are you constantly being the life and soul of events? Practise allowing others to be the centre of attention. Encourage others to be the funny one for a time.

Equally, walk away from situations that are too stimulating and straining, if for no other reason than for witnessing your own discomfort and addressing it will sooth your heart.

Lastly, and importantly, know that your heart can overcome much heartbreak, if you allow it, by facing into the whole experience and do not top and tail the full extent of e-motions.

When your heart is in trouble on physical levels please become your own governor – in other words find out about the real roots of the issues behind your high or low blood pressure, high cholesterol, inflammatory state, nutritional deficiencies, drinking, excess partying or lack of fun. Support your own well-being by doing your research and seeing what lifestyle changes you can make to support your heart.

Summary of the Heart chapter

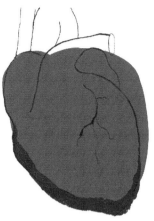

Heart

The Heart is associated with the Summer Season

The element is Fire
The colour is red
The sound is laughter
The odour is scorched
The emotion/energy is joy and radiance

The function of this organ is as the Supreme Controller, the office of Lord and Sovereign. The radiance of the spirit stems from it.

Associated organs are:
triple burner/thermostat (Chapter 7)
small intestine (Chapter 8)
pericardium (Chapter 10)

A balanced Summer provides the ability to:

- Give and receive love with appropriate degrees of emotional closeness
- Knowing how and when it is ok to open up or shut down to others
- Deciding how much to open up to others in all different forms of relationships

Behaviour that shows up when our fire is out of balance:

Compulsively cheerful	to	miserable
Open and overly sociable	to	closed and isolated
Clowning	to	earnest
Vulnerable	to	over protected
Volatile	to	flat

Chapter 10

Discover your

Pericardium

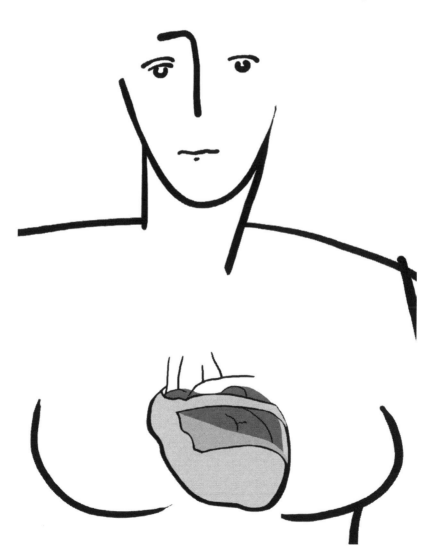

Humour Is Perhaps God's Grace in Action

Discover your Pericardium.

The Pericardium represents the civil servants within your very sophisticated system; from them come joy and pleasure.

"I have gone totally flat. It feels as if my whole chest area has just caved in. It is as if any protection between me and the world has gone out to lunch. There is no buffer. I am tearful, as though I have become shattered glass.

There is nothing wrong in my present circumstances; in fact, I am madly in love with an incredible man. We are getting on really well but I suddenly find myself wanting to run away and hide. I am frightened that I will sabotage this new relationship. He does not deserve that. What on earth is happening to me? Have I hit my menopause early or what?"

This woman's symptoms included agitated sleeplessness. As soon as she fell asleep, she would wake up startled as if she had been suddenly hit or fallen, having missed a step. She was urinating more frequently as if she had an infection, while her doctors said she did not. When she closed her eyes, she had the sense of slightly spinning. Her appetite had gone and she was lifeless, unable to concentrate on anything. Her joy had left her. She had spontaneous sweating in her hands and across her chest almost as if she had a fever, but knew that she actually didn't. After I spent time with her for a while, a story emerged that explained to me what was happening.

It is our Pericardium, our inner guard/gate that is the last line of defence in protecting our hearts. So, alongside the triple burner, the heart continues to function evenly with both what we call the inner and the outer frontier gates, literally and energetically opening or closing according to our needs.

When we have old and unresolved issues of the Fire energy and some genuine love comes into our lives, there will come a point when we can, unintentionally, project on to the new object of our love any old hurts or wounds. Trust versus betrayal are paramount issues to the two gates within our system. So, when we are betrayed by life, love or events, rebuilding trust in ourselves, lives or others will feel incredibly precarious. Our minds will try to control any new experiences of pain and close off the gates to true intimacy, thereby keeping hurt trapped around the heart area. So, ultimately, the energetic sledge hammer of another real love will sometimes break down all that controlled energy.

I have had so many men and women of all types of personality describe, in their own unique way, that the very thing that they craved, which was another love to arrive, would then result in feelings of weakness and a loss of control. An overwhelming sense of vulnerability would arrive that had them startled and shaken up. However, if, as it was my job to do, I could find out what their previous experiences were around betrayal of trust, immediately they were able to see the connections. It would become clear to them what was happening, as their own bodies were both trying to expel old sediment as well as trying to protect them from more pain in the present. Intellectually, it was easy for my patients to grasp that none of us can have a life guaranteed of no pain, so new love does come with risks; but, to live in a closed off state was going to cause them much more long term damage than taking the risk involved in trusting again; then, allowing intimacy layer by layer to enter.

Shock of any sort can have a battering effect on both the outer and inner guards to our heart energy. The body is so clever, though that it does have several layers of the equivalent of security, so it can and does withstand small, medium, and large shocks all of the time. However, a sustained battering or a shock that really devastates and penetrates into our guard system is dangerous for us. It is like when the Queen of England woke up to find that a man had somehow got past all the security and was in her bedroom. That story ended safely, but patients that have come to me are faltering on differing levels under the weight of shocks.

A farmer arrived, sent to me by his daughter. His herd of precious cows, valuable to him personally and financially, had to be culled when the bovine disease had arrived. Mad Cow Disease devastated farms in 2014 in the UK. Thousands of herds had to be killed to stop the spread of disease. In very quick succession, this dear man had lost his wife to cancer, as well as a son in a hideous and freak riding accident that had already, in his daughter's words, sent him "over the edge" , to such a degree that she did not think he could come back from.

Although she knew that she was adored by their father, this daughter also knew that there had been a very special bond between her brother and her father. Her brother had been due to take over the farm six months after the accident. The entire family was shaken but almost relieved about the death of their wife and mother, as the chemotherapy treatments had been so brutal on their mum and had eroded the quality of her life so much so that when she died, peacefully and willingly, it had not been too much to accept.

However, when the freak accident happened to this family's son and brother, the family was shaken to the core. The daughter was already my patient, so I was able to help her through the shocks, even when the farm was suddenly cut off from the outside world apart from the "hideous but kindly inspectors and vets," as the daughter described it to me. She stated, "My father cannot take any more. He has shrunk before my eyes. Nothing used to faze him, but now he is almost gone. There is no light at all left in his eyes. I want to howl when I see him. I cannot bear to lose him, too, although it seems as if it's too late, as he is not there anymore."

This wonderful man arrived who was in his late 60s, but looked well into his 70s, if not older. I could tell that a smile had not ever been far from his kind looking face. He would have been a man at peace with his world and happy truly tending to his beloved herd. So, to have lost everything in such quick succession had left him totally bereft. He had collapsed under the weight of the shock. The dark panda circles under his eyes exposed the lack of sleep and as he sat in front of me, he was repeatedly clasping his hands and taking shallow breaths.

"The most shocking thing is that I cannot pray any longer. I have always experienced God to be tangible to me. It was as if he was always with me on the farm and in nature. Now, there is just this numbing void in everything. I cannot even stand up straight any longer. Without Amy, my son and my herd I am lost, although I am so incredibly grateful that Amy was dead before we lost Paul. That would have killed her, as she lived for me and our two children. When the vet told me that all the herd was going to be put down, I literally just slumped to the floor. He has been our vet forever so he knew exactly all that had happened. He dreaded telling me. Even though we knew that it was inevitable, when the time arrived it was the last straw; I had nothing left in me to withstand one more loss. My daughter is convinced you can help. How? I am gone inside, as if I am already dead. I do not want to leave my dearest daughter though. It would be too cruel of me and I am not that selfish."

With treatment, he was able to transform all that had happened.

He had even helped other farmers who had wanted to take their own lives as a result of the devastation of their livelihoods gone. He had never realised that his daughter also wanted to be involved with the farm. So, with both of them pulling together alongside his treasured son-in-law, they were able to rebuild another herd. His daughter produced two fabulous little twin girls and a boy in relatively quick succession. All were adored and doted on by their father and grandfather, who continued to come to me for many years. His sparkle had returned and he was able to live peacefully with the devastation of his losses.

It was he who one day coined this chapter heading.

"Do you know Catherine, that God's grace is all around me, even more than before these terrible series of events? It is so old-fashioned to even have such faith, but if you have it there is nothing old or new about it – it just is. I knew I was beginning to recover when my humour returned, as despite everything, 'humour is perhaps God's grace in action.' Those two little girls are always laughing so much and although their little brother is quite a solemn and serious little thing, he lights up with his sisters. What little miracles I have now in my grandchildren. My faith has been restored and I even trust that one day I will understand what seems totally unfathomable to me now. Isn't it extraordinary to think that I can honour my son and wife by returning to the grace of having humour in my life daily?"

Another story on this subject involves my mother.

Our dear practise manager knocked on my treatment room door during a treatment so immediately I knew it must be serious. After I opened the door and excused myself, she whispered to me that my mother was on the phone and needed to talk to me right away; it was urgent.

So, it was surprising to hear my mother weeping and clearly hysterical on the phone with uncontrollable laughter. She was the most amazing person to be around when she got a fit of incredibly infectious laughter; it would permeate through and around her like bubble bath that had escaped way beyond any constraints of a bath.

"Darling, it's Grannie."

I had left her that morning with the intention of us scattering my grandmother's ashes after I was finished work. My mother had the most terrible relationship with her own mother, who was almost the worst type of bully that I had ever come across so far, let alone the work that I had been doing with some battered and abused spouses. In fact, my mother, when speaking of Grannie, always referred to her as "your grandmother," and never as, "my mother." There were some roses named after my mother's famous godparent and guardian who had become her and her brother's formal guardian after their father, his closest friend, had been killed. The specially-named roses had a significant chunk of my mother's garden, so in her will, Grannie insisted that her ashes be scattered in her daughter's garden amongst the roses. My mother did not want any part of her mother anywhere near her precious garden, but she was too frightened, even after her mother's death, to disobey what had been put in the will.

"Mummy, what do you mean about Grannie? What has happened?" I could hear huge gulps of air being taken in as she also was spluttering as if trying to spit something out of her mouth. She was laughing so much and so completely that it was almost impossible to hear what came next.

"Darling, you have to help me. The problem is that I suddenly thought I would not wait for you to get this job over with and behind me. So,

I took the ghastly ashes into the rose garden, determined to just be done with it. The problem was that the wind, as I threw the ashes, turned and the ashes flew all over me. I have your grandmother all over me."

There was a loud spitting sound, as she clearly tried to get the ashes that I quickly realised were indeed all over her, out of her mouth. All I could think of was how incredibly outrageously funny it really was.

"Okay, Mummy, is anyone around? Can you just drop all your clothes to the floor of the kitchen and immediately go upstairs and shower your mother off of you?"

Even though it was very funny, I realised how much shock was actually being released through my mother, so she literally hadn't got a clue through her laughter how to respond. Mummy was someone who never asked for help, but in that moment, even through her laughter, she really was asking. To have the ashes of her loathed, but more importantly feared mother all over her was both too shocking, whilst also oddly cathartic, which she badly needed witnessing. Afterwards, she said something that echoed the farmer's words.

"Do you know, darling, that I think God was having a laugh with me? As your grandmother was in ashes all over me, I began to lose all the fear pent up inside me. My terror at times of her just started weeping out of me in the hysterical laughter. I did not know how healing it was to lose control through laughter. Humour has been God in action today mending my heart."

Unglamorous Tips for Glamorous Living Or Tantalising Teasers

For God's sake, or for the sake of whatever you do believe in, never, ever take anything or anyone for granted, as you never know what the next moment is, and then the next moment – or the last moment. For the sake of all that protects your own precious heart on all levels take care with your interactions with those that you love. Be what the action of love is which is consistent. Manners on a consistent level are the WD40 of relationships which need our care, for our sake as well as the people we are intimate with.

Believe in the power of your own internal security system to guide you through the most devastating of times; but, do not try to get through too much by yourself. When and if you hear yourself acknowledging that you are beaten up by life, seek help. Chinese medicine lends itself well to helping deal with shocks to your systems, but there are other very gifted practitioners who will hold the space for you to be witnessed enough to resettle after shock. You need to find someone who, if at all possible, has also begun to thrive again after terrible shocks. When your Pericardium energy becomes willing to be restored, you will find the right person. Be gentle and kind to yourself and take it seriously how much shock you might still be in. Even if your trauma occurred years ago, make sure that you are really willing to be restored and even strengthened through the shocks of your lives.

We really are far stronger, braver and more inspired than we mostly dare to believe so if you are unhappy in your life allow the answers to come to you about why not. The answers will be far more about you, than what you may have assumed they were connected to. For examples about your finances, state of your relationships or some illness, or the state of the nation. The odd thing is that as you discover more about yourself and the more you learn to steer your own amazing mind, body and spirit as one you will truly discover how brilliant your life can be.

I mention a few books here that are full of vital information when you, or your loved ones are going through devastating times around Cancer and life shocks in general. I include Cancer as the numbers of people it is affecting are going up all of the time. So these four books are good to have in your library.

- 'How To Starve Cancer', Jane Mclelland
- 'The Cancer Whisperer', Sophie Sabbage
- Lifeshocks', Sophie Sabbage
- 'The Metabolic Approach to Cancer', Dr Nasha Winters & Jess Higgins Kelley

All these books were written by three incredibly brave and inspired women. They all faced into stage 4 cancer diagnoses and refused to die. Instead they have become pioneers for our generation, leading the way in differing ways. In the midst of devastating life threatening shock they found ways of outwitting what was and is currently, apparently, still not possible.

Jane McLelland's book carves out the new way forward medically to, as her title says, Starve Cancer. She has dissected the roots of the cancer mechanism on the chemical and physical level, whilst being emotionally robust enough to know her responses were appropriate and spot on to the incredible injustices, cruelty and carelessness with which she was treated. She has experienced at first hand the very unpleasant side of what does happen in medicine. She is resilient and gutsy in a way that shakes, what is still predominantly a man's world in dealing with patients of the opposite sex. This book has so much insight into understanding cancer so thoroughly, which is a miracle for all cancer patients and a massive, necessary, challenge to the medical world. The powerful 'revolution' that she is bravely promoting has to now be given legs, with integral medical practitioners learning from her book. They have to be prepared to have open minds to properly help people from unnecessary suffering.

Sophie Sabbage's books transform the emotional, psychological and 'Life shocking' terrain of becoming a patient, and someone willing to radically take responsibility for their own life. Teaching that 'shocks' need vitally to be felt, experienced and then transformed into inspired living. Shock is the number one mechanism that can and does turn our body against itself. It is frighteningly underestimated, so Sophie's willingness to share her own journey and stories with such profound and ruthless honesty is a gift to the world. Her work to empower patients, so that they are not just allowed but encouraged to work alongside the practitioners, is so important.

Both these pioneers are bringing to the marketplace information that has been sorely missed for far more than the 40 years I have worked in and around the Cancer world. Sophie's book creates a way of being a witness to unsaid terrors of such a diagnosis and the absolute insanity of the "false positive "brigade where life is really concerned. All three books are written from very differing perspectives but are equally valid as vital information when your life is on the line. Dis-ease is a combination of physical, emotional and spiritual elements, and should not be considered as being caused by one element in isolation.

Meeting Dr Nasha Winters is an incredible privilege as she is so resoundingly well and vibrant in every fibre of her being.

All four books are beautifully written by women willing to share the realities of their inner, and outer journeys to help and support others in equally unpleasant situations as the ones they had to negotiate.

Keep your chest area covered in dicey weather. The Spanish do not understand why tourists are so quick to strip off when the summer has not properly arrived, as they know to keep their chests literally covered up so as not to get chest infections or colds. They know that wind and the cold weather will hammer their chest areas quickly so they do not expose them to the outside until they consider it to be the proper time. Even in what we in England would consider to be blissful temperatures compared to our normal climate, they will work outside with vests on. So, to women reading this: expose your chests as consciously as you can, putting glamour second to your own integrated health!

It is fashionable for young people to be mostly underdressed during cold weather, as they want to show as much of their bodies off to possible future dates; however, the price they pay with absorbing too much damp and cold cannot be stressed enough. So, please be wise with the weather and think through what and how you are doing when you are dressing. I know I sound like a nagging and concerned parent, but it comes from having had so many patients who are adults and yet they still do not consider how vital it is to wrap up properly in differing weathers.

When you are dying your hair pinks or reds, please take extra care of your own Fire, as you are possibly compensating for your Fire energy feeling low and lacking in self-loving. A very dear friend had her hair dyed bright pink with the shock of knowing that her precious sister was dying suddenly. During the short three months that it took for her to lose her beloved sister, and to the horror of their mother, she kept her hair dyed. It delighted both sisters and gave them some light relief in the horrendous situation that was so suddenly thrust upon them.

Be aware of needing to have ample fresh air where you are exercising your body. If you are able to, walk regularly when you can. Take stairs and not lifts. Find every possible way of not being too sedentary. Refresh your chest area literally with breath.

Practise not giving your inner authority over to anyone else. Allow yourself the regular habit of assessing where you are steering. Where is your journey taking you? Are you prepared to go through the initial hassles, challenges and grieving involved and necessary to keep edging yourself forward to what your personal goals are?

Are your noticing that you have stopped laughing so much? If so, set yourself a goal of perhaps going beyond your comfort zone and taking yourself to the movies, a play or listening to a comedian. No excuses, just the commitment to 'treat' yourself. Knowing that actually the word 'treat' is exactly what you are doing. You are treating your own Fire season that is not giving you a sense of humour and lightness about your days. You almost certainly will not feel like doing any of this, which is exactly when you need to gift yourself by going beyond your resistance. Firstly though, and importantly, if you know that your humour has gone 'out to lunch', for longer than a few weeks, then please seek help to find out why. Many people have delayed emotional responses to situations so cannot understand why when everything seems 'fine' that they are not. Please do your homework and take radical responsibility for your fire, ultimately your heart. It could well be the beginning of a serious energetic imbalance that needs your attention.

Practise getting into the habit of telling the truth to yourself and others.

> The truth shall set you free! Hiding behind a mask may not be serving your or others.

So, when and if, for instance, people say to you, "How are you?" people typically do not really want to know. However, in my experience it is more that they do not want to "feel" more uncomfortable than they already are. So, if you need to now tell your truth in new braver ways to own the fullness of who you are, how do you get around this? You can say things like, "Thanks for asking. Pretty tough day today but it's okay. I'm handling it very well. How about you?"

Implement one of these changes at a time. Allow yourself the feedback that your own body is going to start giving you. Treat your own body the same way you would a new love affair. Be diligent, careful and thorough, taking nothing for granted. If you want a great lover and companion, it is worth the wait and patience involved in really sussing out if someone is right for you. In the same way, getting to know your own body is the most important project of self-love that you will ever do.

You may have so many reasons, conditions and belief systems around your own relationship and view of yourself and your body. You may not have had anything yet that has humbled you and allowed you the blessing of no longer taking your body for granted.

Summary of the Pericardium chapter

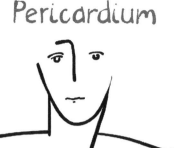

Pericardium

The pericardium is associated with the Summer season

The element is fire
The colour is red
The sound is laughter
The odour is scorched
The emotion/energy is joy/radiance

Pericardium: The Heart Protector, representing the civil servants. From them come joy and pleasure

The associated organ/function is:
Triple burner/Thermostat (Chapter 7)
Small Intestine (Chapter 8)
Heart (Chapter 9)

A balanced Summer provides the ability to

- Give and receive love with appropriate degrees of emotional closeness
- Knowing how and when it is ok to open up or shut down to others
- Deciding how much to open up to others in all different forms of relationships

Behaviour that shows up when our fire is out of balance

Compulsively cheerful	to	miserable
Open and overly sociable	to	closed and isolated
Clowning	to	earnest
Vulnerable	to	over protected
Volatile	to	flat

Chapter 11

Discover your

Stomach

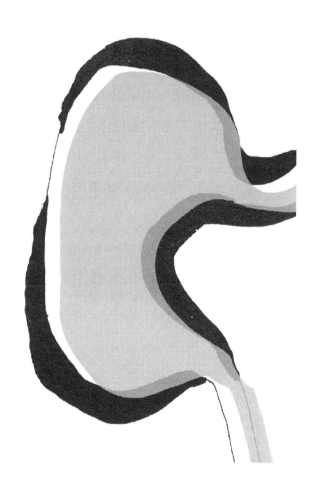

Kickbacks every time we go forward

Discover your stomach

Our stomach energy is our controller of rotting and ripening.

The colours that are associated with the earth within us is yellow, which can be seen clearly on our faces when the earth within us is out of balance. The texture of the skin on our face will also clearly indicate the natural flows of rotting and ripening that is or is not going on.

In the English language we have expressions like
"I cannot stomach it"
"I haven't the stomach for being a nurse"
"We have all been kicked in the stomach"

Our stomachs are widely now known as our emotional centre and in some senses it is also the real hub of our mind too.

With mindfulness now coming into fashion on the one hand it is leading to a far wider understanding of the power of our thoughts. However, on the other, it limits the understanding fully of our entire energy system.

"Do you mean to say that my thinking is not responsible for my feelings?"

Immediately the question is framed in a way that separates the actual continuum of energy and our life force. So the very simple answer to a linear question is:

"No, not in the ways that are now being taught."

According to how well we are able to "rot and ripen" the content of our lives, on all levels is actually how well our thought processes operate. Then according to the levels of life force, or energy that we have, dictates how well our own feedback mechanism is working. With all of our feelings, and emotional states being wrapped up in a whole ongoing process. It is our late summer season, our earth energy that enables an automatic state of sympathy or concern for others.

The words emotion broken down is e - motion. Our feelings and e-motions give rise to the flow of our own energy system. Everything is interconnected. To some sympathy is an immediate act of, where applicable, a hug or touch. For others it is the action of immediately finding ways of feeding hot food to others in times of crisis. It can be a silent level of companionship or a cup of tea. The vibrant health of the earth dictates a response from one person to another almost being unavoidable.

So no amount of thinking will produce sympathy on an authentic energetic level if the stomach energy is too low, stuck or too swamped for instance.

So an integral part of our earth's needs are noting the levels of real abundance, harvest in our own or another's lives. Then being able to choose much more consciously what we do or do not do. How we respond or not, how we interact.

When the earth is very out of balance in the energy of the patient then there can be the sensation around that person of being in sinking sand. You find yourself wanting to be supportive but no amount of support, outside of a clinical situation, really goes anywhere necessarily fast. The energy can be sticky and appearing to be needy. On the one hand their energy seems to push you away, whilst on the other there can be tales of endless martyrdom with resentments that their needs are not being met by others. The way that their energy system is currently working at the time of the interaction is actually producing the thoughts that are in this instance martyred. Until the energy is shifted in all senses and released to do what it is created to do usually the person will revert back to what is the origin of the 'thinking process", an imbalance at the level of the earth, late summer season.

A child was brought into one of the clinics that had become the one where a lot of children came to see me. I shared these practices with the best partner that you could ever hope to have. She was, and is, a remarkable friend to me as well as a business partner, in what I still think were the happiest of working times that I have had so far.

She oozes a peace, calmness and sense that there is nothing but hope and love in the world. So our clinics were also full of laughter and fun whilst incredibly ill patients regularly arrived. Our patients and clients paid us the complement of coming early so that they could soak in the atmosphere. We also had a fantastic practise manager, Betty who we adored. She was as snappy and glamorous a dresser as she was brilliant with patients whilst keeping us fed, watered and on track in every possible way. The children loved chatting away to her.

This particular child was streaming with snot which his mother did not seem at all interested in doing anything about. He looked distressed and really uncomfortable as if in a sort of permanent cramp.

I remember feeling slightly fussed about the size of his mother as I wondered how on 'earth' the very small treatment room would manage with us all.

"Would you like to come through with Tommy?"

"Nope, I will sit and read. You deal with the little rascal"

Seeing the relief on little Tommy's face I hoped did not match visually at least my similar sense. Normally I would have insisted that the parent come too, but on this occasion I wanted to take the opportunity to follow my hunch. His mother slumped deeper into the sofa having piled her large lap with magazines, making it clear to Betty that she was not going to chat. With a wry smile I thought walking away 'she does not yet know the healing grace of Betty' who I knew would not be bullied or intimidated by this poor mother's clear self-disgust or her misery that almost spun out all over the practise rooms. It was so tangible and Betty had seen many like her before. It was very extreme in this woman's case as the oxygen seemed sucked out of the clinic.

In the treatment room I got us sitting down, but deliberately was on a very low stool so he was higher than I was. He was 5 but looked 3.

"What is your favourite colour Tommy?"

Surprised he immediately started chatting away about almost everything.

"I 'ates yellaas, like me Dad, but we likes rainbows"

After a little while I asked him how often he got the bear growling and snapping in his stomach. Again surprised but now totally relaxed he said with actually a tear dripping down his now cleaned face.

"Mostly a lots."
"Is it very sore to go to the loo?"

"Mmmmmm VERY"

"Does it take a long time?"

Tears started down his handsome little face, with relief though clearly, as he got the chance to express what was the most dreaded part of his day.

"Ok, would you like me to use these tiny pins or would you like me to use the Angel energy wand to help your clever body?"

"Booff pease"

"Ok. Shall we begin making friends with your darling and clever bear? He needs our help you see; he is growling and wanting attention"

Big smiles and now excitement - so we made our own little time of magic and stopped the bear snapping. This poor little person was full of heat in his stomach energy and was not able to go to the loo without burning, cramping pains which would have produced searing agony for him.

In Integrated Chinese Medicine there are ways of seeing the energy dynamics between a mother and her child. It was imperative that I find a way of treating Tommy's mother, also in order for him to stop getting the "kickbacks', of her unresolved issues. Her stuck and stagnant energy was the real cause of his symptoms. Partly through neglect and partly through what I suspected and wanted confirmation of by somehow being able to treat her.

The chapter heading has many meanings. One of the kickbacks that this young brave little boy was going to have as I treated him was from his own mother. They both clearly had what we call a yellowing, puffy and damp look on their faces. If I was only able to treat what was a part of his mother's symptoms and the signs of her distress then he was going to keep getting part of her kickbacks. I needed to see if we could deal with the neglect, stop her from feeding him dairy products for a while and hopefully putting him to bed much earlier in a peaceful room with no lights on, and without a TV blazing in his room. All of which was contributing to the Bears growling. Lots of small but vital details had come tumbling out while I treated this little precious child.

The art of vibrant well-being is to begin to master what I call the kickbacks that go on in all of the processes that we have going on. In fact to get to the point that we actually begin to welcome them as the necessary part of our progression.

The ripening of our lives into something that gives our skills, passions and gifts expression is on endless layers of rotting also.

As we go and grow forward there are endless cycles that we can go with, or endlessly be caught out by.

This little boy was a victim of his mother's lack of education and her circumstances. She also had the energy field of someone that lived with very toxic shame, so it was very likely that her vast bulk was protecting her from what had already taken place and for which she was now stuck. Stuck in a constant rotting cycle rather than bearing fruit to become ripe.

I asked her if she was able to bring her Tommy back in two days.

After they had left, whilst writing notes I asked what I experience to be the Divine, that I knew worked with me in the treatment room, to find a way of me being able to treat Tommy's mother.

Two days later when she arrived she was different in that she looked at me directly and said rather gruffly

"I am not sure what you did to Tommy but he hasn't been such a rascal. Do you think you could do anything for me?"

"Let's get you booked in as soon as possible and find out"

Betty, who had already done her own wonderment on this woman, immediately found a slot and asked whether she could come in ten days' time. I knew that would be a huge stretch for her, but would be a part of her then being able to hold out for something that she was now curious about. It was unusual to get such a space of time necessary for a new patient .The normal waiting time was six weeks, which usually weeded out by necessity, anyone who was going to waste precious time not really wanting what I had to offer. Making sure that each patient was properly looked after meant being very clear about how many new patients I was able or willing to take on every week. However sometimes it was imperative that we be flexible, and with two people at least at stake, Betty created the spaces.

We were endlessly taught that every action from us was part of treatment for the patient. So as far as the earth energy was concerned I went into making each and every patient feel properly cared for and nurtured in ways that the world is not good at, at present in many places. The earth energy does not respond well to instant gratifications and temporary solutions.

Ten days later she spent two and half hours with me. For the first time in her life she was able to unpack the festering rotting wounds that were constantly cycling and being recreated in her energy field.

The totality of our clever bodies means that until something is processed through and brought to the ripening stage we have to keep having it be in our systems. So literally there is a kick back cycle which needs to be respected and allowed to go backwards before it goes forward. We generally know it also as the 'one step forward and sometimes two back or five forward and three back'. In some medicines it is known as the Law of Cure. It is a consolidation process that needs to keep being worked with and through.

My patient's underlying energy block came to the surface quickly as I had a sense of what was trapped inside her, so I carefully invited her to spit the 'undigested and rotten' out.

She had been sexually and violently abused by a group of bullies at the age of 11. They had cornered her in the dark whilst she was walking back home. She was almost left for dead. A family friend had found her as he walked home, taking her to his home which was close by. They rang her mother, who came immediately. After they had stabilised her initially, they both talked through how her father, let alone her brothers, would respond if they knew. The father had a trigger fuse and would not have hesitated to take the boys and their fathers to task in a way that would result, almost certainly, in more devastating loss. More importantly though they would lose her Dad to a prison sentence. Both adults were so distressed but able to keep thinking in ways that she remembered made her feel safe and steady while her body vibrated with trauma, shock and now self-disgust. If they told the police her father would have to know. She remembered being hugely relieved on the one hand and on the other, was left not knowing how they could avoid him knowing. Every time she thought of her father's reaction she knew that she felt worse about that, than what had happened to her. It took a lot to have her father's fuse go but no one ever wanted to see it again after the firework display incident of years earlier.

As an aside I never did find out about the firework incident. The art of listening and questioning is sticking to the job at hand and chasing the clues that will help you support the patient, rather than get tripped up by loose ends or curiosity about unfinished sentences.

She did not want to have to see the boys who would be in her daily school life thinking they could get away with their behaviour at best and at worst carry on bullying and taunting her. She was amazed at how much steadiness was returning to her through the actions and steadiness of her mother in particular. In a bizarre way she was able to think very clearly. She had never seen her mother in such a state of shock and had never been so clear about how fiercely she was wrapped in love. She later came to recognise the deep wisdom that had emanated from her mother, who had shown her how she would indeed be able to recover somehow.

Years later she was able to reflect with me how her mother was already robbing the bullies of their power to destroy her by showing her precious child that indeed what happened was terrible but that she could and would recover. She could see her mother praying internally all the time that she was administering so gently to every single aspect of her. After her mother had cleaned her up, with tears pouring down her face, tutting the entire time and saying endlessly "My poor pet, my poor pet. You will be ok but not yet, not yet. Over my dead body will they rob you of your life. That was evil that was done to you. I should have been walking you home. I will never forgive myself."

The two adults paid her more attention than she had ever known in her entire life. She was not in her body any longer and was observing from a safe and less physically painful place. To be in her own body, that no longer felt like hers, was abhorrent to her. She had been badly ripped so again there were discussions about taking her to hospital. Although she knew that she was in searing pain she felt so numb that no sound of distress was coming from her mouth. They were so concerned to not make her life even worse and actually included her as if she was an adult - of course partly in the space of a walk home the experience had propelled her into a terrifying adultness. It was making her feel so grateful to be included, and she understood the terrible worse consequences that would take place if her father knew. He adored her and everyone knew that she was his favourite child of his five children. They had decided in the end to call their mate, the local bobby, around to the house. Immediately he came around, so they discussed what on earth to do.

"Pet, we can't be telling your Dad or your brothers, you do know that don't you?"

Paul, the local policeman, knew every single person in the little community, so he gave his suggestion.

"Your Dad will take matters into his own hands and will not stop taking his idea of justice out until he is satisfied. He, and they, will not be able to be rational. As it is I am barely containing my own rage, which right now is not going to turn back the clock or help you. Your brothers would blindly follow your dad, and we would have a blood bath on our hands as well"

"What I want you to do when you are ready is have you identify the boys for me. I have a mate who I trust from another region who will sort out these kids and I can promise you that they will not know what has hit them, they will never ever touch you or anyone else again."

"Even though I am off duty right now I need to ask you if you want to press charges. If you do then we will do it that way. We must respect your decision."

At 11 she suddenly had three people, all of whom she trusted, waiting for her decision. She was in a surreal bubble, bewildered by it all on every level. Her voice returned as she spoke, increasingly eloquently, as the pus of this rotting event tumbled out. It was as if a detonating device had gone off in every single part of her, as the events were fully witnessed. She carried on speaking.

She was pretty, apparently, she later discovered, but unaware of it and so happy in herself until that moment. Five boys had ripped into her as they jeered and sneered at her in the mud. Once the third boy was jammed in her she stopped fighting as she kept getting kicked at every time she fought. They were crazed and on something, she vividly remembered seeing in their eyes, which were bloodshot and not focusing properly.

So many thoughts had tumbled out of her. In a stream of odd consciousness they fell on to her body as she hovered above looking at the scene that was all about her in the centre. She realised that no one knew that she was no longer anywhere near her body.

Although she was right that they did not know that she was not in her body, they were all noticing that the light in her eyes had gone. Only years later had her mother broached the subject with her and told her that her eyes had gone listless and haunted them all. As they desperately struggled with all their own responses to this appalling event they instinctively wanted to stay focused on her needs, not having the tragic event turn into more and ever widening tragedy.

How would she ever be able to look at anyone again in the face. She already was having difficulty looking at her mother, the family friend, Dan and the policeman. She was in a film that she wanted out of, reversed and eradicated. Would her own body ever be hers again? Why, oh why, had she begged to be allowed to walk home by herself. Why her, why? She felt so dirty even though her mother had washed her gently in a warm bath.

At one point she was so deeply in the memories of it that she was talking as if she was there again. As she talked I had the distinct feeling that she was actually coming back into her body.

It was so vital that as she talked I kept myself grounded and deeply connected to my own earth to be of real and lasting service to her. I breathed deeply and calmly which, even as her breath was beginning to be ragged and hesitant, she begin to almost mimic.

She had been so protected up until that fateful walk alone, that it was she who had begged her mother to let her walk the short distance to her home from the school. Up until that moment there had not been to her knowledge any incident like this. The boys were new to the school and had quickly taken over with bullying tactics. There were three from one family, and had picked up two stragglers from the same form. The headmaster, she later discovered, had already had a teachers' meeting about them and was already considering what to do with them. The same policeman had been called in to discuss the options as the headmaster did not want them disrupting the whole atmosphere in the school. They all thought that the three boys were addicted to glue, pulling in some of the most vulnerable into their gang.

I could tell that with each detail that she had clearly been able to piece together she had been putting her shattered earth back together again.

In a voice that she no longer recognised as her own she told me that this is what she choose to say "I do not want to go to hospital mum, if you think I don't need stitches,I feel ripped, but we can trust

Doctor Smith, right?"

"I agree about Dad and the boys, they would end up in prison over this as they would want to kill each boy"

"So no, I don't want to press charges but what are we going to say about my walk and the cuts all over my face and hands?"

The sound of her own voice both startled her and reassured her. It was the voice of an adult; all traces of an eleven year old had vanished.

She had never ever seen such unhappiness and what she later came to know as acute distress in adult faces before. She was by now sipping tea with brandy. They all had a cup in their hands. She remembered clearly the details of the friend's wife being away visiting her mother, and so Dan didn't know really where anything, so he ended up giving them what she knew only came out for special occasions. This was a horror story, not a special occasion , she had thought to herself and the little dainty cups were difficult to hold with her still shaking hands.

She had never drunk tea or ever touched alcohol before. She instantly loved the sensation that it gave her. It was so memorable for her that she suddenly felt as if she could and would cope if she could keep accessing how the brandy made her feel.

Her mum had spoken with an idea.

In the end they managed to keep the appalling truth from her father and the brothers by pretending that she had slipped, falling way down a steep edge of the path, where the friend had heard her cries. They told her dad that she had twisted her ankle and that Dan, the family friend, had carried her up to her room, before her father had returned from work. Unbelievably, her brothers had been taken on an outing by an uncle. Although they hadn't always walked home with her, their presence would have prevented this from happening. She even suspected that the attack had been to spite the brothers and that it was partly premeditated. She could hardly walk anyway, so to be still in her room was safe from facing what was ahead of her. She was particularly close to one of her brothers, so she was wondering how on earth she would be able to keep up lying to him, although she knew that everyone's future depended on her doing so.

I let her spill out as much of this festering, unsaid and trapped story as was possible for her. Even though it was an agony for her I knew that we had not yet got to the tipping point for her.

She told me that the doctor had come to check on what her Dad believed to be her ankle but, accompanied by her mother into the room, he needed to check the mess that her vagina was in. Some stitches were in fact needed but he did it in the room with her mother holding her hand and stroking her. The mild sedative injection did help her cope.

She suddenly stopped and took a huge breath. She looked at me trying to determine whether I could be trusted. Searching my face for encouragement to carry on she suddenly blurted out "I am a fat drunk now. I do nothing but guzzle cakes, biscuits -anything that I can get hold of. I loathe myself. I won't even consider killing myself as I assume that I would even cock that up. So I deliberately do it slowly. I am not stupid. I know exactly what I am doing but don't even think I really want it to be different. I don't deserve to be alive or have my life"

"Every single day I wake up promising myself I will stop both the sugar and the secret drinking but then I just carry right on. I am so mean to Tommy behind his Dad's back. I don't know why my husband hasn't left me yet. I push him away all the time"

"Did you start drinking secretly from after the rape?"

"Not quite, but I never forgot what that small amount of brandy did for me. It was a bit later when I flunked the next lot of exams. I was very bright and always top of the class, but suddenly I didn't care any longer, so I was soon bottom of the class. When I did begin drinking I started stealing from my parents and even my brothers to pay for brandy. Every time I drank I would feel as if I was going to be able to cope "

"I even deliberately set up my older brother - who was my best friend- to start hating me. The family joke was that we were really twins, but were born years apart for my mum's sake."

"It tears me apart every day that we literally have not talked now for ten years".

"What happened when you went back to school?"

"My mother, with my permission, had told the headmaster. They devised a way that she could be in the school helping out in the kitchen for my first week"

"I never saw three of the boys again but I still had to face the other two. Something must have happened as they never ever bullied anyone ever again and were put into the boxing club where an ex-marine taught all the kids who were going off the rails. He also knew what had happened and took both of them under his wing. One day he confronted them in ways that actually expelled their shame and guilt. I was curious so one day, years later I asked the Marine what had happened to the boys."

"The headmaster kept an eye on me and it was often suggested that I could have therapy but I pretended to everyone that I was fine. I lied my way through everything and could see in everyone's face either how tragic it was or how confusing and disappointing I was. As I began to put on weight my father just kept looking sadder and sadder as he looked at me with tenderness. I almost hated him for clearly still loving me. No matter what I did I always saw only love and confusion in his eyes. I do not know how to move on or change this. I can see that you are not judging me but are capable of somehow using whatever you do to start unlocking me. Yes, I was raped, and yes, it was appalling but the bit that I loathe and am totally stuck with, is that it is me that keeps up the equivalent of violating myself with my own behaviour. It is as if I am poison and now must continue to poison everyone else. Is that how it has to keep being? The poison is bigger than any rational thought, its stuck in my body, not just my mind."

My favourite teacher used to say that Integrated Chinese Medicine does not fail patients, however practitioners do. That was all I could think of in that moment as this brave, wounded and hurting woman looked at me for confirmation and hope.

"I will use every tool that I have been taught and really want to support you. I believe that you can recover from this. I do not normally tell patients this but it is vital that you know that you are not as alone as you may feel you are. I am not going to tell you what you should or should not be feeling as I understand the mechanism of shame very well. I have recovered from rape and abuse and some of my family members have lived in recovery from Alcoholism".

She looked at me with such gratitude that my stomach flipped knowing that the rawness of shared horrors is already a part of shifting the power that these appalling situations hold over us. Long after our bodies have got going again with so called normal life, there is an energy field that needs clearing. It is like living with internal barbed wire tearing away at your stomach every day.

"I do not have money to pay you after I have paid for Tommy"

Despair and terror hit her face again.

"Instead of buying the cakes that you eat, let's see if you can start baking instead and bringing us two cakes a week for other patients"

She beamed with relief.

"I've always wanted to see if I could bake. Do you reckon that I could?"

"Yes, I do and I think that you will be surprised at what happens with your cooking. If you want me to work with you, are you prepared for what I call the kickbacks? It means that each and every time we unlock some of your hidden energy you will have what appears to be like a worsening on some level, but only temporarily. So for instance, I suspect that tonight you will feel totally shattered, relieved but also possibly terrified, even ashamed that you have shared your truth. You may find yourself almost obsessing about what you have said and what you perceive I will be thinking. I want to see you twice for the first three weeks and if you need or want to ring, Betty will give you my number. If I can, I will be on the other end of the line when you are in real need. Please don't worry as I have never ever known our worst moments be at what you will consider is going to be a good moment for me. The moments of real crisis for me usually come at 3am in the morning and usually take all the courage I have to reach out and ask for help. So please remember that, when you also may be resistant to reaching out. PLEASE have the courage to ring if you need to. I mean it. Someone was on the end of the line for me on many occasions. So for the next three weeks my phone will be right beside me to answer if and when you need me. After that we will make the next plan. Does that sound ok?"

Integrated Chinese Medicine can diagnose where the roots of an issue is. The art of this medicine is finding out which layer will unravel the others. By treating immediately her spirits (her blocked energy) in her stomach where she was still reeling from having the earth literally taken from underneath her viciously everything else had the possibility of falling back into place.

There were many signs and symptoms that also she was experiencing on physical levels which was inevitably being worsened by her drinking and mostly eating sugar. Her body was on the verge of going into the next layer of very serious medical consequences. My sense being with her though was that if her spirit/life force responded to treatment that all the other physical symptoms would also change.

Within six months she had lost 3 stone. The toxic shame that was never hers in the first place had fallen off her. The secrets that she had had to choose and get so caught up in had lost their power and hold over her. She had even been able to talk to her husband about what was really going on. She had started becoming an excellent cook, joined Alcoholics Anonymous, found her self-respect and started loving her child and her husband in ways that had not been possible before. She carried on coming to me for six years until they moved, just checking in every now and again and having me check out her petrol gauge as she called it. She loved coming in and telling me that she was getting used to the kickbacks. Even loving them in fact as it always meant that she was going forward again.

There had been a happy reunion with her brother, where he had told her that he had worked out what must have happened, which Dan had confirmed to him. He and Dan had gone looking for the whereabouts of the other three boys, men now. One was an addict in prison, while the other two had become born again Christians working with troubled boys. They had deliberately gone to meet them as they both sensed that by doing so there might be some sort of healing for everyone. The boys were eleven years old when they went so totally violently off the rails. Interestingly, they visited the man, now in prison, and hoped one day to bring him through the hell he had been a part of. This dear patient, who was now so free in her own energy, was further restored and healed by knowing this added information. She said that all that had been stolen from her seemed to have now been restored. She amazed at how resilient humans are. She became a magnet for people who believed that it was not possible to recover from traumas. Knowing differently, she gently steered them through to what she lived. Carefully she helped others, always knowing that her recovery and peace depended on her looking after her own needs first, then those of her family, then others.

The last time I saw her she was beaming with a radiance that I had so longed for her. She was totally unrecognisable from the woman that once sullenly entrusted me with her precious child.

"I became so curious about the boys that I had had to face at school, that although I had learnt to forgive them I was not able to stop wondering what comes of young people that have been the perpetrators of such terrible things. With my own ruthlessly honest evaluation of my own limits I began to see that they were as much victims of their behaviour as I was victim to their acts."

"Please carry on"

"Well I came to see that we are all so frighteningly capable of the cruellest acts, and to hide behind our apparent differences is a lie that I cannot afford to live with".

"At eleven I was the victim to a series of consequences, which by understanding them, frees me to soberly and humbly know could have resulted in me behaving in those or similar ways"

"I need to live with forgiveness towards myself and others continuously, as not many of us honestly have the total freedom, consciousness or luxury of behaving in ways that we would like to when push comes to shove. They were high on glue and in turmoil from their own wounds."

"Once my brother told me about the three boys and I knew that I never had to see them again I was not able to let go wanting or needing to know more about them. Even though I stopped paying the price with self-hatred and shame, I now understand I needed to know more. No one will ever understand unless they have been in a similar situation. I actually find myself caring about them. You will get this bit I think. That Marine I tracked down who is still working with kids. When he realised how far I had come he was able to generally talk about his method for working with young boys who are so violent and do terrible things at such tender ages. Not all of them are reprievable but an Australian taught him a method of literally taking hold of these boys and holding them in big bear hugs. Looking at the size of this Marine it would have been a big bear hug. He apparently holds them literally until they break down sobbing and sobbing. That then begins the process of them being taken back to their innocence, before they have acted out of what is generally considered to be the "energy of the ancestors ".

"It sounded similar in some senses to what you were able to do with me and my energy"

I marvelled at how she was telling me about two of the rapists as if it was a very far distance memory that clearly held no charge any longer in her energy field. She was even able to make jokes.

Apparently it was a system started in a prison where some of the most dangerous men would be 'accosted' by this huge Australian. He would persuade them to let him hold them in a hug. The way that these men were held by a fellow man was almost always enough to have them break down for the first time in their entire lives. Without exception that would change them completely. So this Marine had broken these two young boys by hugging them and then enfolding them in a disciplined way of venting their frustrations and wounds from their earlier experiences. Both boys had been violently and sexually abused by their own father, who was considered to be an upstanding and respected part of the little community that they had grown up in. They only moved to her community as the local bobby was clearly beginning to be on to how the boys were being treated.

This patient was so intact and had come full circle as she had been able to literally ripen her experiences from the rotting.

She was an incredible cook and started up a successful business after I stopped treating her. She kept in touch for many years so I also knew that she did anonymous work with the rape victims around her who reached out for help.

Hurting people hurt. She was able to ripen through the rotting hurt and stop her own vicious cycle of hurting those that she wanted to only love.

A huge part of her 'earth' becoming more stable once again was the constant source of nourishment and understanding from many

282

other fellow alcoholics. She was able to be a part of groups that allowed her to harness her own potential as a human being and with some deeply spiritual, practical (not religious) suggested disciplines. All the natural rhythms that she had been deliberately going against were able to be reintroduced into her life. Part of her recovery on all levels slowly understood that all humans on a greater or lesser degree are struggling to transform what had been laid out before them, not at all initially digestible or pleasant. By actually finding herself identifying with the violence of her abusers she was able to be fully restored. She would come and share the processes of her recovery with me which was a very humbling position to be in. Something very wrong had been done to her but as an adult her coping mechanisms meant that her own innocent child was beginning to also pay for the endless cycles of unresolved blocks and hurt. As she learnt self-care and self-nurturing choices that aligned more with her family's norm all her family relationships were restored. The earth energy needs understanding, support and nourishment regularly.

The way the French, Swiss, and Italians certainly used to eat is ideal for the earth, stomach and spleen energy. To take time over food regularly with love and care put into all aspects of the preparation from colour, texture and types of food cooked is vital for the wellbeing of this energy field. To bring vegetables from the earth to the table within hours is the ideal. Having gone so far away from that we are paying for the stagnant kickbacks. In some cases where people have low stomach and spleen energy they insidiously can be in states that become like treading on damp swamp land, not going forward but in many cases sliding backwards.

If we take these actual examples of food to the way that we now care for each other, it is of course now coming out in all sorts of ways. In restaurants it is often the norm for couples or even families to not be chatting or connecting to each other, but instead to be on their phones or devices. Experiments have been done to prove that when we eat in front of the TV or are having our brains concentrating on an electromagnetic device, we do not digest as well as if we are in peaceful loving surroundings eating at a table with seasoned food.

So many people in today's economically and apparently sound countries have such severe issues around food. There are confusions around what is nourishment on a regular basis. Eating out of season is very wearing on the stomach's energy. Salads eaten in the winter for instance is not sustenance for the bodies' life force. Once we begin to take on board that our earth affects our sense of being centred, stable and allows for self-nourishment, then in the capacity to nourish others we can begin the process of clocking all aspects of what we are "stomaching".

Rather than being depressing with more overwhelming proof of another thing that we are getting wrong it can be the smallest of adjustments that bring about the most sustainable, re-connections to our own paths of self-loving and self-caring.

A mother who adored her oldest son with an obsessive and excessive smothering had an unconsciously spoken favourite expression "No one knows the hardships of my son, he is so remarkable. It is not fair the world is so against my son. No one understands him"

She almost broke her son with her own projection of her own life. It took her son his entire life to unravel the effects of this broken and distorted projection. Her idea of mothering was in fact, breaking her son's very capable energy. When I met him he was on his knees having tried so many ways of stomaching food. He lived on energy bars and protein shakes and could not trust himself to eat meals around others. Until we started to work together he had not connected his deep frustration with his mother's smothering behaviour and his issues around food. Although he had become obsessed with his physical appearance and was considered fit, secretly he was very fussed about his own discomfort around food.

He came to me as he did not know how he could date the woman he really fancied if he could not and would not be able to eat with her. He had confided to his best friend one night after drinking far too much, which on the whole he did not ever do. Unbeknown to him, his friend was a patient of mine who had been coming for regular check-ups for about 18 months. During that time he had learnt how far the net stretches of what traditional Integrated Chinese Medicine can do, so he volunteered to ask me if I thought that there was anything I could do. Severe and complex allergies are what I was originally told.

When this patient was offered any sympathy about how debilitating his allergies must have been, he brushed it off as if it was nothing. Literally the emotion of sympathy for himself or others was noticeably absent from his energy field. So it, in its absence, was a huge clue to my detective work to support him.

There was sweetness to his smell when it came time to physically examine him. A smell literally pervades the space when a patient's seasons are out of balance.

"Do you find yourself worrying a lot, being a bit like a hamster on a treadmill, not ever really being able to let go of the constant state of worry"

"Yup, but what's that got to do with not being able to eat most food groups now?"

"A lot and I will show you how everything is all interconnected as soon as I can "

His last sentence, as with his others, had been almost sung out of his body. Again with the earth, late summer season, as with all others, there is a distinct sound to each set of organs in the body. There was a melodic tone so his sentences came out like a song.

"When you fly do your legs and ankles swell a lot?"

"Do you perspire on your forehead, arms and legs?"

"Do you get diarrhoea after eating when you are able to eat, or feel full up quickly or even sick most of the time, as well as listless and tired increasingly?"

"Is your sleep restless?"

He clearly felt happier, when in his opinion, I was asking what he thought was relevant.

He was so uncomfortable in his own skin and, it was immediately apparent, desperately ill.

I was so grateful to have been trained so brilliantly as I knew that this man's life was holding in the balance, that so called allergies were the least of his medical issues.

When doing the physical examination and by asking so many questions I had the nasty job of quickly getting him to a doctor. I suspected that something very sinister was going on which he and others would have been oblivious of. When I took his pulses it was possible to tell that he had a very extreme situation going on. Everything was pointing suspiciously to a possible cancer and tumours. Frustratingly in those days I was unable to ring a friendly doctor up telling him what I suspected. In fact we were legally not allowed to ever say we treated cancers or suspected cancers. So without any sympathy or even softness in my own tones I bluntly told him that I wanted him to go to his own doctor that day.

"I want you to give him the list of the following signs and symptoms that you have shared with me and he will decide what tests to immediately send you off for."

By matching his own voice and lack of sympathy, I knew that I would be more settling to him. Instead of the possibility of him churning away with worry, he needed to be contained by me telling him what to do and what was to happen. I rang ahead to the secretary of the private practise and explained that a doctor needed to see him urgently. "May I suggest you do yourself a favour?. You need Paul to meet you there and for now do not tell your mother, if that feels right to you?"

He looked at me with huge shocked eyes, particularly the bit about his mother. He was 35 years old and mortified that I would know somehow about the agony that the relationship with his mother still caused him.

"Hey, do you mean to say that something serious is going on possibly?"

"Yes I do, so we need to make sure immediately what you are up against"

"Shall I go now?"

"Yes. Leave your car in the car park and take a cab to the doctor's. We will get Paul to meet you there if that is alright with you?"

"Aren't you being a bit dramatic?"

"Let's wait and see. I want to be absolutely certain that I have looked after you properly and diligently right from the get go"

Amazingly he suddenly relaxed and even looked relieved as if he already knew what I knew, and just had not had a clue how to tackle his own sense. By being told exactly what to do he was able to let go and stop worrying for a bit.

He did have cancer and immediately needed an operation to prevent a complication that would not have been possible to back away from without the surgical intervention. Paul kept me informed as to what was happening.

Later, alongside the choices that he made to deal with his cancer, which had, unfortunately, already spread. He became deeply empowered by connecting the dots about his mother's behaviour. The idea that we are not affected by others and can live in such insular ways is contrary to the truths of how all of our life force and energy intermingles with each other.

By this man not knowing how to tackle his issues on a level that ever went near the real source, he was only going to get worse. In this case had he not gone to the Doctor that day he almost certainly would have been found suddenly dead.

So without judgment he chose to get fully behind all aspects of what had been happening to his own life force. Inevitably he began to talk much more to me and his new cancer therapist about his constant frustration and discomfort around his mother's smothering and very manipulative tactics. He had felt so caught up in the sticky treacle of being manipulated, hating himself for not knowing how to tackle the dynamics in a productive way. He changed his attitudes towards himself and began to have sympathy for them both. His mother was enraged by his differing actions and attitudes but he had come to realise that although it was not her deliberate fault, her actions were a cause of too much conflict for him. He came to understand that by him refusing to be her surrogate husband, or accepting her smothering, she either was or was not going to face her own wounds and energetic binds. In the absence of her being able to change too, he had to become very conscious of boundaries around her.

There were many differing aspects of his dis-ease on so many levels and degrees, so whilst it was not his mother's behaviour that would or could be blamed for his condition, what he learnt was the contributing factors of his own actions. He took full responsibility, becoming happily empowered to live very differently as a result of what was a devastating prognosis. He lived way beyond any of the estimated statistics for his western diagnosis. Embracing fully what he could and could not do to make changes and become self-nurturing he became much more relaxed and happier. He saw all the signs and symptoms his body had been giving him as attempts to alter the frustration and unhappiness that had been his daily drivers. This in turn altered everything for him.

He loved knowing how his energy was doing and what it all meant. He was one of those patients who felt safer knowing everything that I was able to tell him and not to hold back on anything. It stabilised his earth and helped him produce his harvest from the self-awareness of these continual cycles of rotting and ripening.

The woman he had fancied came forward on hearing how ill he was and they started dating literally over his hospital appointments. They married on a trip to a clinic offering a combination of integrated treatments. He became fascinated by the idea that a lot of cancers are considered to be fungus based so, instead of worrying, he became empowered with more and more knowledge on integrated and fully connected levels.

He lived for a further fifteen years which in his own words were the most productive and happiest of his entire life. His mother, after five years of almost totally fuming, also turned her life around as his stance ended up giving her no alternative. The more he understood that he was not powerless but actually empowered to love his mother, not her actions, the quicker her behaviour was transformed. By not reacting his own life force gave her an invitation to drop all that was wounding her, but no longer affecting him.

Tantalizing teaser tips / unglamorous tips for glamorous living

Our very stability and sense of our own earth, our home life is affected by our stomach energy and vice versa. It is affected by our home and mothering, nurturing connections. We can learn to mother and give birth to our own needs for continual nourishment.

The rotting and ripening of our daily lives on a mind, body and spirit level is always ready to respond, to be supported by our actions. The kickbacks in life always continue.   An example of how small the changes can be, but how far reaching the responses can be, is when people start to eat their last meal of the day before or around 6 in the evening. So many digestive issues on physical levels are really helped by shifting the times and how we eat.

By aiming to find and create the budget for eating organically you will increase your nutritional intake by 40 per cent.

What you eat makes the most extraordinary difference to your daily energy and life force. However being harsh and bullying or even obsessive about it is counterproductive.

Here are some books that I would recommend if you want to begin the journey of finding out how to bring more harvest into your late summer season.

- 'Chinese Dietary Wisdom' by Danny Blyth and Greg Lampert

- 'The Burn', by Haylie Pomroy. It is worth mentioning that the reason why I love this book is that there are three sections, each of which is manageable and packed with really valuable information. The chapter on digestion is excellent in connection with this season.

- I am also adding a recommendation that you find out about Michael S. Tyrrell, Wholetones CD's. The healing frequency music project is a very powerful tool in healing the energy tangles in your earth, and also other areas. I have put it here as earth energy being out of balance can lead to such a profound misery around food, cooking, kitchen space or just generally cherishing ourselves, so this is music that is very soothing to our systems. When my stomach just did not know how to cope with food and I could not settle back into all the new aspects of a recalibrated body, I listened to these tapes. I was also endlessly falling over, with terrible balance issues before I started listening to the music. After I had listened for ten days I noticed I was staggering less and had improved balance.

- Stop having dairy products, peanuts, oranges and bananas if you are feeling congested. Experiment with these foods and see if it makes any difference to your breathing and sinuses (if having any issues with them).

- Please seek out help properly if you are suffering from Bulimia or anorexia before you get to the point where you are in such denial that you will not even want help. How we manage our relationship with our food is a massive aspect of our earth season but, as much has been written about this in other books, I wanted to cover aspects that are not necessarily discussed. Focus on your relationship with nurturing and the 'harvest' of life from the perspective of what this chapter has talked about.

- 'When Children Grieve' by John W James and Russell Friedman with Dr Leslie Landon Matthews is an incredible source of information to retrace our own earlier lives and may be worth spending time getting to know what may have affected you as a child, in the way of trauma. There are so many ways in which we end up not absorbing the harvest of our lives.

- Be mindful about being around people who simply cannot celebrate life properly. Watch how people eat and what sort of nourishment they are able to allow themselves and others. Work out how important it is for you to eat in a relaxed, harmonious atmosphere.

- Please put ways to celebrate your own achievements in your diary regularly. Do not wait for others to acknowledge your milestones for you. Equally, make a point of celebrating other's successes.

Summary of the Stomach chapter

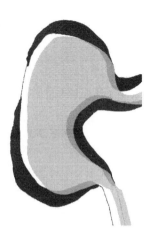

The stomach is associated with the late summer

The element is Earth
The colour is yellow
The sound is singing
The odour is fragrant / sweet
The emotion/energy is sympathy/ overthinking/worry

The function of this organ is our controller of rotting and ripening. It is responsible, along with the spleen for storehouse's and granaries. The five tastes stem from them.

The associated organ is the spleen (Chapter 12)

Balanced Late Summer energy provides the ability to:

- Ask for help, taking in nurture and care when it is offered to us, not pushing it away
- Distinguish between when it is appropriate to look after our needs and when to care for others.
- Give support and nourishment to others

Behaviours that can become evident when the Late Summer is out of balance within us. These are the extremes that we may sense in ourselves or others:

Smothering/mothering	to	not supporting
Excessive dependency/co-dependent	to	over-independence
Not centred and dispersed	to	stuck and heavy
Over dependent on security of the home	to	inability to put down roots
Feeling needy	to	repressing needs

Chapter 12

Discover your

Spleen

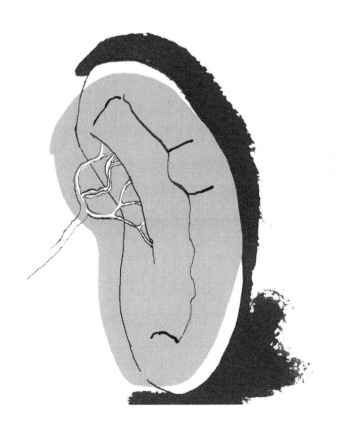

The divine in all things, very particularly the seemingly unforgivable

Late Summer

Discover your Spleen

Emotion: sympathy/overthinking/worry

The spleen energy is called the "transformer and transporter" of all food, drink and substances in our bodies. The season is associated with the late summer, which conjures up fields that have had their abundant growth harvested. The harvests have been transformed and then transported to where ever they are needed.

"I have never forgiven you for not using that very good brain of yours and going to university," my father's very good friend roared at me on my arrival at a ski resort he was staying at. It was close to where I was convalescing from more surgery, this time it had been over 20 hours long with three surgical teams rebuilding my lower spine, and removing broken screws. They had been broken for six years.

I was not sure whether to be flattered by his reference to my brain, or furious. He forgot the fact that I had been taken out of school when I was 13, put into hospital for six weeks and then put to bed for a year. I had never returned to school. I am not sure in his fury that it would have occurred to him that I had no formal qualifications. After all, I was the daughter of his quite formidable and brilliant best friend, so he would have, and obviously had, made massive assumptions - assumptions based on the veneer of life having been taken for granted. My mother certainly never mentioned to anyone how ill I was, partly because she really did not believe I was, and partly because admitting it would have been more for her to be deeply disturbed by.

My father would have been much more honest and focused on my well-being, so I was totally nonplussed that his closest friend did not have a clue about the consequences of my lack of education. He was still, in part, responding to my mother's unflattering marketing about me. No one knew that I had also experienced sexual abuse and other violations going on from, in part, one of the medics that were being entrusted to look after me.

Why would I even think of telling a mother that did not believe any of the physical pains that I was in? It was made very clear to me that anything that had happened to me was my fault. I was at a very young age fully formed as a woman but totally ill equipped to pay the prices it extracted, with no safe haven to learn how on earth to defend myself, let alone how to behave with a body that seemingly was like being a walking piece of succulent meat that many wanted to own, capture or possess.

Cruelly, the language and game of one of my relatives that we saw a lot of, goaded us all into claiming our "no" and our boundaries, only for that same relative to then roll straight over them. This same relative interestingly was without a functioning spleen. So, at a young age I learnt that any form of self-protection or boundaries actually made my life far worse.

My life was a permanent helter-skelter of utter chaos with sexual abuse being one of the many horrors thrown into the mix. Terrifyingly, in the absence of attention or acknowledgement of my existence from my mother, I was craving attention so no doubt I far more easily accessible to be preyed upon. Harrowingly, I was living in constant physical pain with medical symptoms that had to be daily negotiated. To add to an unbelievably complicated picture, any of my medical struggles could so easily have been triggered under the umbrella of a myriad of external causes. For instance, just to name a few: the divorce, the breakdown that my mother, by this time, was considered to be having, her increasing alcoholism, being blown out of my bed (yup -a real explosion that ripped the entire Embassy beside our building completely out), let alone now not being a part of any groups that children normally were a part of by their attendance. These were all red herrings as to what was really happening to me. Any possibility of nurturing, transforming or transporting from networks, was slipping far away from my reality, worsened by my own mother's inability to think about any of my needs, let alone wants.

To those who did not see me as a piece of very edible meat, I was someone that would and did listen to others. In the midst of a childhood that I, like most, thought was "normal," I equally thought that it was part of everyone's experience to be talked to or at by almost everyone of any size, colour, background or age; it did not seem to matter what the circumstances were. People would tell me their deepest secrets, fears and worries. No matter how young I was, the stories came out. What I myself was indeed having to transform and transport, to earth and stomach, made it far easier for me to listen and not condemn, whilst tuning in to what it was that I could do to be supportive to whoever talked to me.

Lacking in any confidence at all, as I was in a more or less constant stream of verbal humiliations and put downs (apart from my father and early on from my brother), it was rather soothing for me to know that others were also having beastly times. To then know that others felt better for having been with me was heartening on the one hand but bizarre on the other, as my own mother would go to great lengths to avoid spending any time with me and constantly spoke disparagingly about me to others. It took me many painful years to realise and work out that it was herself that she was not able to hang around with, which is intellectually an almost certain fact. However, it did not help the emotional pain of rejection that ripped hard into every single day of my childhood.

I worked out very early on that whatever love really was, that it was the only way out of all and every situation. It also never ever occurred to me that we were not all interconnected to what I know as Divine energy or source.

My constant internal dialogue with what I experienced to be part of the very matrix and fabric of the seen and unseen was and is so real to me that a constant dialogue, not monologue, continues to this day.

The deafness of my early childhood made it all very clear to me what lay in the mystical fields of silence, even the differing tones in silence. It was not at all confusing for me to hear distinctly the voice of what I reasoned could only be God. Being brought up on a farm and watching nature carefully with the guidance of that distinct voice that was a part of, but also separate from me, illustrated the rhythms of our earth and the world.

I vividly remember realising that in the absence of my mother being able to be loving what I needed to do was to love her nevertheless. To remember our essence is nothing but love, and yet also is a lifetime's ambition or, as many believe, lifetimes is always our salvation. It is the only real way to transform any victim stance as becoming loving demands from us that we put down our dramas and our reactivity. We learn to act and not react from the deep centre that we actually all have waiting to be ignited. When our self-respect and self-love expand into every single corner of our being, we merely notice that another's behaviour is not likeable or is inflammatory, so we begin to know what to do. In the most extreme of circumstances, I have been able to know that to be the case. To imply, though, that it is easy or merely a trite plaster to be dabbled with, is missing the point.

Many people have what is called an open spleen, which very simply means they are gifted and cursed simultaneously with being able to feel into others' emotional and energetic states. Until they are able to tell the difference between what is theirs and what is not, they often carry others' unexpressed baggage, thinking it is theirs.

The energetic rhythms of a balanced spleen allow for boundaries around the sustenance, and nourishment of self and others in relation to our needs. So, years before I was to be trained more formally in the deep philosophy of Nature's systems, I was having experiences that showed me how profoundly difficult and traumatic so many people's everyday lives were. It was comforting in some ways as my own life seemed nowhere near the chocolate-box-happy-family scenarios of the films. On the surface it looked glittery, glamorous and opulent, yet underneath it I was punch drunk, not having a clue what I was doing.

The nature of the balance of our spleen is partly set according to our individual connections to our mothers. I had this extraordinary visceral knowing that if we had been in the animal kingdom my mother would have eaten me. She would have been in such extreme chemical trauma on giving birth to me. It would have been a normal response to eat the young that would not have survived anyway. She was swimming in a genetic soup that she struggled with and which had led her to Alcoholism and other forms of self-medication. Society hates the idea of a mother not being what it assumes is the normal, nurturing and nourishing type of parent. So when in fact a child is not being cared for, it is not so bizarre that often that same parent can easily manipulate the systems to make out that it is the child who is at fault, difficult, or tricky. In the profound difficulty of not knowing how to love me she had to make sure that others saw me as a problem.

My father passionately saw, knew and loved my mother to his dying day. So, as I adored my father, it was not so difficult to feel into what was behind her behaviour, aimed at me. I vividly remember working it out that she did not love me but that I somehow loved her, which I realised internally would be my salvation. So no matter what she did, deliberately setting up ways of me being bullied, humiliated and endlessly rejected in fantastically cruel ways, I used to see what was happening. I had no idea that by doing this I was dismantling any victim stance. Deep internal knowing was empowering me step by step, whilst also building up the energy of transporting and transforming, although it did not seem it so at the time.

To add to this bewildering picture, my mother had an incredibly magnetic personality; she was very dynamic, well-read and brilliant. Although easily bored by her own children, she was fascinated by most things and was thoroughly irresistible, fun, with an outrageous sense of the absurd and a sense of humour.

The more I realised how unloved and inadequate she felt in and of herself, the more I was able to build on what seemed impossible for so long. I stopped losing my temper with her in utter desperation as I stopped feeling so triggered. I even worked out that she insidiously would rile others to express her own seething rage, misery and confusions.

The earth and late summer association, in balance, is impartial to what it gives birth to so it does not discern between good or bad. Altruistic behaviour comes from a group or a person who expects nothing in return for their behaviour. We are internally compelled and propelled to nurture in ways that, if not expressed, hurt us or the group; this comes from the energy of the earth being in balance. The earth does not think about endlessly producing season after season products, flowers, blossom, harvests – it just simply does produce harvest.

The emotion connected to the earth is sympathy, also translated as worry, concern, thought and obsession. So, when the spleen energy within us is functioning at its optimum, it is compelled to lean in to producing the harvest of concern, thought and sympathy for the natural processes of life.

People often talk as if understanding someone or something condones behaviours, whereas I believe that the real truth of any situation, actually understood properly, robs it of its sometimes detonating affects. We are set free once we can detach with loving forgiveness from behaviour that is driven by complex webs of toxicity. We can salvage our own parched, swamped or overgrown land from the many thieves of a lack of nurturing attitudes. By understanding what is really going on, not condoning the acts or behaviour but being better prepared to deal with the truth, we can be aligned with what nature does.

Sometimes the land has become so parched with the first rain after a drought that it does not penetrate the earth; this too can be true of love at first. With no expectations of the timing of love being able to penetrate a parched person, eventually love will penetrate deeply. Equally, as our own earth and internal land stabilises, we can find endless ways around the land masses of others. Loving action and our own energy systems find ways to interact with others' reality, detached and yet connected to them. Not only does the time come when we are not so affected by them, but we can influence others just by our energy system and its rhythms. For example, a woman's menstrual cycle will automatically start conforming and altering to the other women in close proximity, so that shortly they are all menstruating at the same time.

My mother's thoughts, energy and focus were always around the obsessions involved in addictions that transformed only momentarily her overriding state. Her agonising pains, the festering wounds from her own childhood triggering her self-hatred, managing a body that would not have given her a moment's rest from differing taunts of malfunctioning, and pains on all levels had to be managed somehow. The self-hatred that drove her and was so triggered by me, more than almost anyone else, was a hungry internal wolf tearing her apart so viciously, so she was never present to be sympathetic, except to strangers. It was odd getting used to the fact that she would and could be strangely tender, kind, incredibly funny and so thoughtful to almost anyone that she did not know very well.

Years later, after her death, I read in my mother's dairies an account of what she knew she did to me. She knew and yet was not able to stop herself; in and of itself it was a sick but soothing medicine for her own ailments. It worked temporarily and kept her need for self-hatred going. Shame works that way.

By knowing my mother so well, I learned to respect and admire what she did continuously achieve. In some ways, as I managed to really separate her behaviour from her, her addictive personality traits from her real essence, the more I loved her.

When the stubble is burnt without fail every year, as was still the norm in my childhood, the earth does not have an opinion either way at the collective wisdom of the farmers as the first match is lit. When I would ride over the burnt stubble, I would marvel at how nature would be receiving the trace minerals of the ash into the earth as the ploughs would turn the earth over. Years later, of course, I understood that the regular and equivalent burning I was in was actually making me stronger in my ability to produce harvests. Little did I know that what lay ahead of me was going to need some pretty intense transforming and transporting from the spleen energy.

On the most mundane but vital levels of transforming and transporting her own needs, my mother was constantly stuck. She was suffering from the same very rare connective tissue disorder that we now know has certainly affected at least three generations of us. This meant that her own internal tissue matrix was struggling massively – and, tragically, she never knew it. Her body was shredding all of the soft tissue in her body increasingly, after giving birth to me, in out of control ways. She must have been continually bewildered, frustrated, even at odds as her body did not ever lead her to believe she had any "earth" to stand on. It would have seemed like she was drowning in a swamp some of the time, whilst also her earth had barren aspects and mixtures of harvesting, that were not sustainable for her so there had to be kickbacks.

Part of our Earth energy allows us to distinguish between when it is good to look after our own needs, and when to care for others; my mother endlessly got these times muddled. She appeared to be maddeningly incapable of nurturing us and yet generous to a fault with nurture for others, if in short generous bursts. She had a brilliant mind and yet was often lacking in mental clarity.

One of the main features of a functioning spleen energy is the capacity to think with clarity. Acupuncture points for exams are based on the spleen energy system. When the Spleen is in balance our capacity to think is functioning at its optimum. My father in particular showed me how to use my brain, my intuition and inner knowing and to not be frightened to think everything through carefully. He was a big communicator so he allowed me to constantly find my way through what was happening.

The late summer season is ideally a time of the harvest having been picked, collected and a time of celebration for what has been brought in from the fields. It is a time of understanding that now the fields may need to be left fallow for a season to replenish the earth.

As for my darling mother, she died knowing that she was loved and loveable. Her wounds and her disease had not prevented love from being what both love and nature are. At the end, she even clearly wanted, trusted and actively sought out my help and nurturing. She got total focus of mind at the end and in very clear sentences penetrated through the fog of her life. She looked at me one day and connected to me in a way that had never been possible for her.

"Darling are you in pain all of the time?"

"Yes, Mummy, but it is something that I am used to and has oddly brought me closer to the Divine in all things."

"I can see that, darling, but actually you always were connected, even from when you were born. I was afraid of the light that shone through you. I did not feel deserving of either of the two of you. I tried so hard to destroy you but, thank God, I never succeeded. The thing that stuns me is that there is no bitterness anywhere in your face. I look for it, as it should be there, but it is not. You have never, ever stopped loving me, which I hated you for and yet now I understand. Thank you."

My mother died 48 hours later.

There are forces beyond our control and ultimately whilst the one is a neutral, but ever changing force, the other is something that is inherent within us and finds a way - finding a way through from the seemingly unforgivable to, of course, the forgivable in all things. Every single event that ever happened has shown me how resilient and amazing our integrated beings are.

Unglamorous tips for glamorous living or tantalising teasers

Tips for a healthier energetic state of the spleen - or more tantalising, teasers for the spleen energy

When you catch yourself spinning on your hamster wheel of overthinking, force yourself to watch a movie, engage with anything that will help your brain stop.

When you catch yourself not being moved by something that requires you to be sympathetic, clock it, as it is a sign from your own internal system that perhaps you have not given yourself enough attention or asked for it from others. Or, perhaps you have by passed a need somewhere along the line.

Be mindful of what you are craving in life and in your food groups, as often you are actually allergic to the very thing you desire. Or, you need to be mindful of a possible mineral or vitamin deficiency.

Be willing to continue to know yourself well enough to catch setting yourself up and or others with overfilling your plate, literally or figuratively. Being a 'tomato' (martyr) in relationships or connections usually leads to frayed situations, so become equally happy with saying "no" as saying "yes" to requests from others. Vitally, really begin to know the difference between your 'No' and your 'resistance' to people, places or things that do require you to grow through -transporting and transforming.

Be ruthlessly honest with yourself when making a choice in your actions. Are you using your thinking, being spontaneous, or compulsively acting out in your choices, unable to think through the consequences?

Chinese dietary wisdom - eating for health and wellbeing by Greg Lampert and Danny Blyth is fantastic book to help you to treasure your spleen with food.

Too much raw and or damp-forming foods with irregular eating, on the run, all strain the spleen energy.

A damp environment is also not good for your spleen energy so if at all possible at the very least make sure that your bedroom is well aired and make it a priority for your health to get rid of any damp patches in your home.

Summary of the Spleen chapter

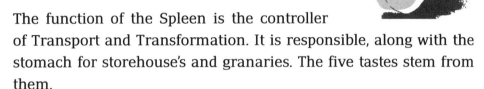

Spleen

The spleen is associated with the late summer

The element is earth
The colour is yellow
The sound is singing
The odour is fragrant/ sweet
The emotion/energy is sympathy/ overthinking/worry

The function of the Spleen is the controller of Transport and Transformation. It is responsible, along with the stomach for storehouse's and granaries. The five tastes stem from them.

The associated organ is the stomach (Chapter 11)

Balanced Late Summer energy provides the ability to:

- Ask for help, taking in nurture and care when it is offered to us, not pushing it away
- Distinguish between when it is appropriate to look after our needs and when to care for others.
- Give support and nourishment to others

Behaviours that can become evident when the Late Summer is out of balance within us. These are the extremes that we may sense in ourselves or others:

Smothering/mothering	to	not supporting
Excessive dependency/co-dependent	to	over-independence
Not centred and dispersed	to	stuck and heavy
Over dependent on security of the home	to	inability to put down roots
Feeling needy	to	repressing needs

Chapter 13

CONCLUSION -
MY SILVER THREAD

We can create what some call luck or our own Midas touch, which is the equivalent of what I call my silver thread.

Every single function that we have in our mind, body and spirit operates as one. The more we master our own incredible 'being', the more we can influence our own walk through life. If we really want what we mostly all do say that we want we have to begin to fully take on board how integrated everything is. We so often live though, in direct contrast to our wants, as if getting on one side of a seesaw and not finding the counter balance is somehow not our responsibility. We can so often ignore the obvious boomerang effect sooner or later of all of our actions. In evolving though we can get to the point where we begin to take, what I call, radical responsibility for all of our life. Not just some of it. We really are designed to be able to be at peace and happy, and not because everything is like a chocolate box fantasy in our ever changing lives. We can deliver to ourselves an increasing level of knowing that we are in a 'win/win' situation, trusting in the balancing that has to be going on all of the time.

We can even begin to influence hugely what and how we are living, going from sometimes feeling as if we have just been tossed in some terrifying seas and not being able to swim, to actually thriving and living with increasingly levels of choice. Now the greatest inner wealth that I have gained and practise is the power to choose, over and over again how to respond to the events, people, places and things around me. I work WITH my amazing mind, body and spirit, no longer AGAINST the bits that I had been taught to cherry pick!

There are many more solutions than we normally know how to even stretch towards. Putting the endless complications of how religions are presented aside, what we believe to be true is what actually becomes so, if, and when, the belief is energised for long enough by us. With an increased sense of how to expand through layers of dis-ease our beliefs will radically be altered. What we would have thought was simply not possible becomes more than possible. I mention this as a huge aspect of my work is to share and awaken others to what is beyond their present belief systems. The shifts have to take place on visceral or kinaesthetic levels for us to be renewed, energised and revitalised. One of our biggest stumbling blocks to our daily living is thinking that we "know", things, people or information. So when we begin to live in the freedom of not knowing then life becomes an adventure of endless discovery. In my own case my father taught me from so early on to question all things and to use the 'muscles of my brain', as it too, needed exercising!

As I finish this book the tissue in my hands is disintegrating, along with my eyesight being affected from more compression in my neck, probably needing again more surgery. As I turn my head to the right there is evidence of compression and collapse. Suddenly I find myself under three more consultants a cardiologist, a vascular and orthopaedic consultant with urgent requests to have scans. It is a shocking development that again will require patience and quietness to distil what really is important and to not get swept up in anything except action, rather than reaction. How will I choose to respond to this next bit of what these particular syndromes are about? Has my silver thread left me? "Hell NO", as a dear friend says in her Virginian drawl, that always reminds me of the raspberry ripple in ice cream, of course it has not, if anything it is stronger and clearer these days. This syndrome is doing what, in some ways, it is primed to do, so actually it is a question of me 'choosing' consciously to do what I can, to steer the consequences, not giving it too much space to invade the increasing levels of peace that I do have.

My inner peace does not have to be affected by the 'casing' that I live with, which is struggling more and more. I can in fact love myself more and listen to what is needed next. I can choose to energise all that I love and believe in, all of the next solutions. Being able to be alive is way beyond what has been expected at so many points so each and every day is the most stunning adventure of wonder, even with all the low points. It is humbling to realise that not that long ago in history I would not have been alive at all, let alone flourishing as much as I do or having the freedom to write this. To also know that I would have been burnt at the stake for having the life, experiences and trainings that I am privileged enough to have today!

Life forces us to relinquish control in a variety of ways. However, it is those times that, as we are brought to our knees in so much turmoil, we are shown by the world that we must run from pain and discomfort, escape from ourselves and self-medicate our pain every which way. We are taught that pain is our enemy, and that there is more wrong with us than right, so before the get go we are overwhelmed. No wonder we run! We are not taught that pain is actually merely part of our experiences and something that we are fully equipped to deal with. There is an expression which is relevant in this context "You will not be able to avoid pain in life but suffering can become optional".

We are certainly not taught that when we are brought to our knees by life, that it is a fantastic new journey and adventure into living life on life's terms. Our burdens can end up becoming at times a joke and we lay them down at what to many is called the Universe, God, the oneness. We have to let go and deliver to the unknown our not knowing or understanding of what on earth is happening. As we let go, more we begin to thrive as best we can in the God particles of not needing to understand anything. Yet paradoxically we begin to know more than we have ever previously known. We are freed the more we get to know ourselves and the language of our mind, body and spirit.

The power of our belief keep us tangled until we examine them one by one. Without shame or guilt we can wake up to knowing that we are not just our biggest stumbling block to vibrant living, but therefore we are ALSO our solutions. There is more than enough of everything to assist us once we become our own best friends operating our own incredible systems that actually are constantly wanting to serve us.

Please look at your own life if you are reading this far and look honestly at how much you too have come through. The more our self-worth grows and develops through mastering our own being the more we can see, feel and experience our own lives in such freeing ways.

An equivalent of a silver thread, luck or your own Midas touch will become obvious to you. With that awareness of how extraordinary your own life is, a never ceasing fountain of gratitude will be running through you. This in itself can become part of your own engine fuel. It can end up coming from a deep well of awareness to all those who have contributed to your own wonderful precious life, at times even getting you through your nightmares. As I was writing this I was staying with an incredibly inspired woman who has created "Making money fun", she was born on a Friday and on the 13th! She has for sure created her own Silver thread in the midst of incredibly challenging and heart breaking circumstances. I do not think that I travel far these days without meeting amazing people who are transforming the realities of their lives with increasing inner wealth.

My brother's birthday is on the 13th. He for sure walks with his own Midas touch. He will go to any lengths to help out others, which very early on included being put in jail in the Sudan. He was in such trouble for helping out two damsels in distress that he had two nights being told that he was to be executed in the morning. He was to later foil medics and life herself by surviving being thrown 140 feet from the impact of a bike ride with his body being stopped by the road, having bounced three times with his helmet only staying put for one bounce. I was told of the accident having just arrived back from India to the UK. A very persistent lady in her office in the Cedar Sinai, Hospital, in Los Angeles, kept repeating to me, "Please do not get on that plane to identify your brother's body if you think he will be alive. He will not survive the next few hours. I have been told to prepare you for what all the medical team are sure about. There is far too much fluid in his brain"

I equally persistently kept repeating that "he will live". I had never been surer of anything in my whole life. How was the poor woman to know that I had waited for this call, or that I had been flown in to the UK from India under, by any stretch of any imagination, extraordinary circumstances? It was very clear to me that I was brought back suddenly to the UK for exactly this call. He lived, seemingly against all human odds.

The silver threads have never left us and we are clearly both still supposed to be here, against some, would say, terrible odds. However that is the point of this book. We all have our silver thread that when understood takes us through circumstances that are supposed to be, mostly, transformed.

All of life brings opportunities for us to become what we are more than capable of being. It is said that "life is an inside job".

So the point is that we actually all have our own Midas touch. Our own energy can literally create or break our days. It takes time to get to know ourselves and a willingness to go beyond the narrow interpretations that keep us stuck. There will be times literally, or again metaphysically, when we do experience being in a type of prison. However, even then we can find ways of continuing on the inside of ourselves with transforming what is our inner terrain, which then in turn does affect the outside.

Someone once asked why on earth I smile a lot, when they knew that I was in pain. "It makes me feel much better and is an incredible discipline in gratitude, which needs to be practiced the tougher things get". Although to be grateful to all those mentioned over the next few pages is permanently easy, and has not required any discipline. Nor do I use the word, grateful; lightly as it has become a visceral knowing of gratitude, of how truly amazing all of life really is, with also how amazing we are.

So many people have contributed to this book without even realizing it.

My father continues to influence me every single moment of every day. He was the most extraordinary of human beings; courageous, wise, ferocious at times, kind, gentle and understanding of the human condition. Long before my training he was already teaching me and showing me what service to one another was really about, therefore the very nature of what humans need. He produced a son that is, as equally remarkable, and compassionate.

The family dynamics with my on-going health matrix created many perfect storms. Storms that have eventually propelled me to give birth to this book. So I am very grateful to all of the emotional, spiritual and physical fires that have alchemized a life of heaven here on earth, even through the patches of sheer hell.

Without four outstanding surgeons I would not be here at all, let alone walking or having been able to return repeatedly to such a remarkable life. So huge thanks go to Steven Garfin and his team in San Diego and particularly the amazing Liz Stimson. The first time I met Mr Garfin he said he would operate, when no one else would touch the complications and mess my spine was in. Over twenty hours I was rebuilt with him orchestrating three surgical teams. Then later, again it was his expertise and precision that brought me back around to the "lights are back on again", after my spinal compression had me compromised by over 75%.

In the absence of being able to have a remotely functional family life, Steven, with Liz and their team provided the functional means for me to make it through many an operation. Obviously I literally carry their work around in me, but more importantly I walk daily in loving gratitude for what they alone facilitated. The respect and love I was shown made me far braver than I felt often. Bronek Boszczyk for the remarkable surgeries that he did over two days that even amongst his colleagues said could not be done. I trusted both surgeons implicitly, with their calm presence being like bathing in the highest levels of what some humans do and can attain that of truly being what greatness is.

Both Steven and Bronek so often touch the equivalent of Angel wings, that they both have a presence that is not worldly, yet the truly remarkable aspect of being with either of them is the tangible humility and humanity that they conduct their work with. I so often think about you both with such amazement, frankly, that I was so blessed to have been under your care. Your presence is so loud in its total absence of a blustery ego that you can be felt as you arrive in a corridor of a ward.

Dr. Jurgens, the anaesthetist, who delayed the surgery by hours to make sure that everyone understood how incredibly dangerous my conditions are. The arrogance of what can sometimes take place

318

was replaced by a thorough and complete willingness to listen and to keep me safe. Thank you so much for listening and hearing. Massive thanks for restoring my faith when it had been really shaken in the medical world.

Mr. Shah, who untangled the mess that a disabled, rotated pelvis and hip had created, thereby allowing the previous surgeries to settle so that my body could recalibrate my brain and body functioning. He also has an air of greatness and majesty about him that is a soothing balm when you are his patient. Thank you also to precious Rhonda Rosier who was always efficient and wonderfully kind, as well as thorough in her backing up of Mr Shah.

Special thanks go to Dr Hepburn, who wades patiently and meticulously through the complexity of these conditions. I leave his presence laughing as we have faced together the next precarious hurdle. He never fudges, shies away from, or gives me the sense that he wants to tidy me off from his workload. Together, with his expertise, we face the next very probable hammer blow, methodically cutting out any unnecessary tests or knee jerk reactions.

Thank you very particularly to Denise Pearl who so often has saved the next emergency moments with her absolute dedication to her work and helping, truly, the patient. I will never forget you and even the other day again and again, as the incredible ANGEL that you are, you, catalysed a result that we needed so badly. Thank you.

Professor Khullar, who has had my back in numerous ways teaching me and helping me live with Mast Cell Activation Disorder and all the endless and very unpleasant complications that come with it. He has taught the surgeons, anaesthetic teams how to go forward without killing me. On more than one occasion, after his incredibly long days operating on other patients, he has had to stop everything to help the teams looking after me. He has done so with huge grace. On one occasion one younger surgeon in one of the operating teams arrived at midnight to thank me, as he had been learning from the Prof, via phone call, what the condition I have means when surgery is happening. "What I have just learnt tonight because of you and the Professor is going to save others' lives, thank you. I am sorry that it has to be at your expense though. I totally underestimated what you go through, for which I am truly sorry. I did not have a clue about Mast Cell Activation Disorder. What the Professor has taught me tonight is a massive game changer". The Professor also has remarkable dedication to his patients and his work, somehow making us all feel as if he has all the time in the world, when we all know damn well that he has far less than most. I know so many of us that are so grateful for your kindness and ability to make us feel important, and really cared for in our suffering, that you clearly mind so very much about. Sadly a very rare occurrence for most of us.

Thanks also to his amazing team who keep us all looked after from the endless administration side. Special thanks go to Helen Connor who has been wonderful in her endless patience. Your work behind the scenes is hugely appreciated. Abe Nyanteh also who helps Helen at times.

So many people provide a network of scaffolding that holds these extraordinary consultants busy and demanding lives together, including the loyal families who often must end up feeling like a second consideration to the endless demands made on what is to them, THEIR wife, father, husband. Massive thanks goes to all the administrators and medical teams that are in the 'Health' professions.

I am often asked why I am so at peace when I know suddenly

that more surgery is required or more tests. My intention is to immediately see how I can serve those that are going to be helping me. Inevitably there will be a nurse or someone that needs some gentle consideration or just a smile of appreciation. My attitude is my choice as I actually know the systems so well now that mistakes will be made because that is the nature of what the human experience is about. So my peaceful attitude comes from accepting that most people that have such a huge influence over my prognosis are sincerely doing their level best to help me. I can be as conscious of their needs as much as my own and therefore sway the odds in my AND their favour by participating fully in all the exchanges that will be taking place. I do so with as much love and care as I ideally want to be treated, fully accepting that some people are not yet awake enough to be loving or careful, YET. Nowadays I am much more focused and interested in "can I rise to the challenges of being loving, kind and careful with each and every interaction. Am I willing to be present to the presence of each moment mattering?"

Professor Mathias who was brilliant enough to have me finally diagnosed properly. I call him the POTS master. He is very clever and curious about the human condition so has also retained his humanity. Thank you for also helping me realise that clearly my mother and grandmother had the same condition, with differing manifestations.

Dr. Driscoll, from POTS CARE, who managed to help me become more of a semblance of myself. In one week she managed to give me more expertise, time, attention and inspired knowledgeable help than almost all the consultants that I had been under my entire life. Thank you is not enough of a statement, so I hope and pray that in some small way inviting you to share your knowledge with others in 2019 is at least me sticking to my word. You made it possible for me to keep dreaming about a future which would always include seeing if others could be helped as you have helped me.

Dr. Tim Evans, thank you for being 'normal', emotionally intelligent as well as full of humour and with an astute cleverness that you are humble enough to give others credit for. I am grateful for you taking me on and not running too far when you see me booked into your day.

Barrie Savory, I still think that I first came to you when I was a very young teenager. The story of you saying to my father that you were sure "If I was a cook baking a cake and I stuck a skewer in to this cake half way through cooking I would swear that I had left a vital ingredient out. Your daughter's body is missing a vital ingredient", was the first thing that I remembered after I was finally diagnosed! Thank you for always being there for me and for believing in me through each and every operation. You have always managed to keep me going far more than it seemed possible on numerous occasions.

Professor Francis Smith, and the brilliant Julianna, you have always made incredibly tricky MRI scans somehow manageable. You have always gone way beyond what I had sadly got used to and made so many impossibly stressful situations somehow manageable. Thank you.

Also when it comes to thanking those that have importantly saved my life physically, let alone on many differing layers of emotional and spiritual saving, here are the equally huge souls that have massively impacted my life force.

Stella Welton has walked for many years through these roller coaster surgeries. I love you and admire you much more than words will ever express. You have never stopped being such a vast part of my wellbeing on all levels. Your enormous spirit has even brought Mandy and then Annie to this project, just in the nick of time to make it possible on numerous practical levels for this book to be born. You inspire me daily with your Grace, humour and extraordinary courage, even from the distance that has become our lives.

Alec Welton for so many influences you have had over my life. Firstly thank you for literally having me in your home when you were newly married. You even participated in me staying alive by intuiting to stay in hospital overnight as you sensed something was going to go dramatically wrong. It did and you saved my life as it lay in a precarious balance. I am not sure that I ever told you that I had actually left my body and was watching you and the nurses from a safe, no longer agonised body. To say thank you is a little feeble considering the enormity of what you have done. That does not even go near what you singlehandedly did for the clinic when I was in America.

Bonnie Rowland for rocking my world with confirming all that I know about energy, love and the seamless borders that are between many worlds. You are so precious to me. Thank you for sleeping on the floor over many nights as my life hung in the balance again and again.

David Rowland and Bonnie, both of you have always given me your friendship, skills and time in abundance. Thank you over and over again.

Carey, for all the support, respect and love you have shared with me. You have supported me in so many ways and never stopped being there for me with your laughter, intelligence and incredible compassion.

Alice Tierney for constantly believing in me and for being the voice of reason in my denial, making me face this eventual diagnosis, so that I could regain some dignity in the midst of the bullying that had taken place medically. My time with you is always sacred and filled with what is the walk of heaven through facing into lovingly what is. You show me how to stop meddling and to find the wonder in all things, including all that we resist. I adore your humour and your presence makes each day seem fun, even when I take things way too seriously. You inspire me all of the time; huge thanks go to you on numerous levels.

Liz Embley who I still and always will, miss so hugely. Every single time I think of her I feel cross that we did not have more adventures and laughs together. We could always talk about anything and everything in ways that made the world so much richer for her takes on it all.

Sarah White, almost a day never goes past that no matter what, we are there to witness and listen to each other, on the end of a phone. You have been steadfast, full of wisdom, humour and wonderful cherished friendship. How on earth we weathered my mother adoring you and putting you in such an impossible position as I bored her so much I shall never know. Except it is worth mentioning it as it does say a huge amount about how inspired you are as a person. She did not really like any of my other friends. Thank you for all the ways that you so cleverly inspired me to keep going through those darkest of times. You are a remarkable woman and certainly walk with your own magical silver thread.

Georgie, for coming back into my life with so much laughter and love. Unbelievable to me at times also, that you epitomize grace, despite many reasons that I can think of, that could so easily have had you become the opposite of what that really means. Also a huge thank you to all those on Monday nights that have contributed to the real abundance of life returning to me. I so look forward to more nights of our laughter and fun, whilst also sharing what we passionately know makes a difference to our and so many others lives. Thank you for making me so welcome.

Maria Dennis whose expertise and Ferrari like brilliance has contributed to this and the setting up of a medical convention that will be pulled off next year.

Jessie Gill who serves me wonderful coffees in mostly freezing conditions, overlooking the glorious sea, and her incredible creations of art, with her signature enthusiasm, quick-witted intelligence and fabulous laughter. You are an amazing human and I love knowing that you exist.

To Jill Tucker who managed to calm what amounted to hysteria as a brand new Mac arrived. I am so incapable of being any good at utilising this phenomenal machine but Jill made it seem possible. Thank you for your generosity of spirit to me.

Tom Freer your amazing light has accompanied me through the darkest and literally last year's so thank you for your wonderful talent and inspired creation.

Thank you to Annie for your help early on in this. Your own life is proof of the courage and dignity of the human spirit.

Huge and special thanks to Sharon Paul, who has been an Angel in so many of our lives.

Anne Ingoldby for stepping in as the angel that you really are, to pull together the threads of my computer illiteracy. When I was losing everything in a dreadful sea of Glandular Fever and infections you arrived as a breath of fresh air and made everything seem possible again. Even though your days are already so full and your workload so immense you have been there for me like a real Wonder Woman. Without knowing it you epitomise what the book is about.

Norma Williams for being the most thoughtful, loving and incredible neighbour we could hope to have. You have unknowingly always turned up like magic with flowers or your wonderful thoughtfulness and by your actions helped me get over many a time when I felt so close to wanting to give in. You alone so often broke up the levels of physical isolation when I was too ill to make new friends. Massive thanks.

Ian, for being the best landlord and therefore huge thanks for your lovely home that inspired me through the agony of recovering from the last six operations in quite stunning of circumstances.

Di Palmer for your huge input. You will not think it has been but it has! Thank you.

Mandy Humphrey, for bringing your unique and exceptional skills into my life. Thank you for having the ability to help my body find its way again through the scaffolding. To find deep rest again and a sense of relaxing on the physical plane that I had long forgotten. You also have proof read this book and made me believe it was all possible with your humour, willingness and vast levels of generosity of spirit. You are dynamic health and wealth in motion. Thank you.

Eugenie, thank you for being another Angel in my life. Your light shines brightly and you have made the world such an infinitely better place by your wonderful beautiful presence.

Rachel and Richard thank you for years of love and delicious real friendship. May we continue to have much more fun in the future.

Many thanks go to Simon Bates-Joyce, a real soul brother. No talk is really necessary when a connection defies age. He has often made it possible for me to get back to writing and remaining focused.

A very special mention to the most inspiring man I know. Simon Coster. Being in your presence is always a privilege.

Gerry and Hermione for looking after me following one of these procedures. Your kindness and generosity is always remembered and treasured even though our lives are so different now. Many thanks for very much, one day DBs Inc will come about!!.

To all my patients, that over the years, have entrusted themselves to my skills. Journeying with you has been a great honour.

To Pennificasious who has restored some good old fashioned glamour, innocence and wonder into a stage worn thin. Thank you. Delicious gluten free Lasagne is bliss. Thank you Rianna.

Sophie Sabbage who allowed herself to keep going way beyond her prognosis. Sophie in the midst of dying entrusted me to keep using my skills, when I was so close at times to forgetting I had anything left to offer. She had the supreme courage to hear me when I had the audacity to just know in my own bones, or metals, that the 'death sentence', could become a 'life sentence' for her. Her books The Cancer Whisperer and Lifeshocks are serving the world mightily, in equal measure to how mighty she has allowed herself to be, as a 'red carpet' has been rolled out for her to walk. You are an inspired, ferocious and brave warrior of the Spirit. Thank God too. I am grateful that you are alive. Thank you Soph. We are still here and got back up together. May we continue to ride more of life, to then have many more adventures.

A big thanks goes to Vanessa, who kept managing to deal with me when increasingly my hair was disappearing in patches and falling out. You even managed to stop me having it shaved as the wretchedness of it going was a stress one to much for me so I was determined to have the beastly drama over with. Jade: you also have been amazing to me. Thank you to both of you for being two fabulous human beings who put people first and care. Your care for us all made and makes a huge difference to my life.

Clare Davidson so recently for just getting me and "it". Your seeing, intuiting, worldly and otherwise skills have catapulted me out and about with a clearer resonance. What fun it has been working with you, although actually it can not ever really have been called work as it was and is pure magic that comes from you.

Katrina - I never travel without your silk elephants reminding me constantly of generosity and abundance in this world. Thank you for far more than can be expressed.

Thank you Tara and Kerrie for being who you both have always been for me. It has always been the biggest privilege of my life to have been a part of your life. You both flew into my heart the first day I met you and have never left. I love you.

Ann Wilson whose immense courage and mission impacted me so hugely by reminding me to not give up on my dreams.

Maxine Hargreaves for patiently understanding that my brain would not compute the simplest of tasks and made "making money fun" a renewed possibility, on the practical levels.

Dr. Linda Brown whose friendship has meant the world to me. In such a short space of time you have become a soul sister. I value all the precious time we have spent together. Here's to meeting you in Nashville soon. You are a phenomenal woman of the spirit.

A special thanks to Po, Diana Cox, who promised Liz that she would keep an eye on me as Liz knew that she was not long for this world, after my mother had just died. She has kept to that promise and unfailingly been on the end of the 'phone or physically visited whenever her incredibly busy timetable of looking after others has allowed. I am so grateful to you Po. You are remarkable and a huge lighting rod in a world that often forgets what really matters.

There have been a few and exceptional Integrated Chinese Medical practitioners over the years so massive thanks go to them all. Thank you particularly to John Tindle. It is always a pleasure to see you and discover all the next ways that you are serving a starving and hurting world. You are a remarkable human being. Someone once asked you why you regularly do some extreme rituals, where you suffer intensely as you master another layer of what is possible for humans to endure. Your humble answer sums you up stunningly: "How else would I really understand or know what people really go through with severe pain, disease and illness".

Over many years I have loved seeing Helen Fielding. I so look forward to our sacred times together and am very blessed to have become one of your patients after the wonderful Hilda Harding.

Charlotte Amy has treated me through the worst years of this nightmare time and never flinched from being whatever was needed, as a first class practitioner of Chinese Medicine. She is a wise old soul, in a vivacious and forever young body. I owe her my sanity as, week by week, she energetically returned me to myself. No mean feat with what had been done to me and how far I was dangling already from the precipice, in mind, body and spirit. Thank you for more than you will ever know. You are the best.

Rianna who has edited this book into the shape it is today. How on earth you have had the patience to wade through the muddle, I will never know. Your belief in me, and total understanding of what I am doing brightened up the struggling and dismissed all my doubts.

Special thanks goes to Robin and Jane Feild for all the help and support that they have given me every which way and being behind me 100%. Despite how impossible I am to photograph, Robin's expertise with his lens won through. Jane, your courage, humour and tenacity are incredibly infectious and inspiring.

Vitally thank you to the serendipity of meeting Min Cooper. Having the same Christian name as my mother is somehow rather wonderful. You have done such an incredible job with all the illustrations. It has been without exception such fun to work with you. Thank you for getting this and the other longer term projects so completely. I adore the illustrations and appreciate meeting you hugely.

Lastly to Richard McNunn who made me believe that I could do this. He is an incredibly smart, funny and genius maverick who lives with huge integrity so I knew that if he was willing to go with this concept then somehow I would pull it off. He is more than capable of telling me that I should stick to my day job, so again every time I was daunted by the vastness of pulling this off I remembered him. You do not have over 200 hundred books under your own belt to not know what you are doing. THANK YOU RICHARD.

Conclusion, or the 'Backwards' as I prefer to call it from Barrie Savory D.O. He has looked after my 'back' since I was a very young woman - and had my 'back' through so much. So it seemed fitting that he finished this book.

I count this as a great privilege to be asked to write a few words about this, Catherine's book. Inevitably, this must include something about Catherine herself, as the book, and her, are inexorably entwined.

We don't argue about much, though we do differ slightly as to when we first met. We do, however, agree that it was sometime long ago, when Catherine was somewhere in the middle of her teen years.

She has always been different.

Even as a teenager, there was the mystery of innocence and knowledge, vying tantalizingly together then as they do now. Though now, with the addition of the wisdom gained through her experience of life, and all the myriad vicissitudes it has thrown in her path, to create a wise and sage practitioner. Innocence must never be lost as it is the key to knowledge. Innocence is the starting point to learning. As her writing shows, she never stops learning, both from her own experience and that which she gains from interfacing with her patients.

I have deliberately used the word 'Practitioner', as those of us who practise outside of mainstream medicine, are all practitioners. The arbitrary titles that our trainings bestow upon us, more likely to confuse than to define, the true role of the health practitioner that we are. This is especially true with Catherine.

There is a passage in her book that particularly illustrates this.

"Life is a constant paradox. To understand that, begins a dance which, in and of itself, sets your spirit free. Your purpose then comes to light with the increasing self-love and self-respect, which can become an automatic step in the daily dance".

With this philosophy Catherine has managed her own life and here has written a book with simplicity and wisdom that can be a beacon from which all may benefit. We do have within us the most extraordinary systems for self-healing. There are no pharmaceutical drugs that can match the power and diversity of the immune system. Nor can we match the complexity of our neural systems that, not only manage our everyday physical actions, but our internal world. The internal world where we control our temperature, our blood pressure, the secretions of hormones and subtle tasks beyond description. There are no manufactured pharmaceuticals that can come close to replicating these internal phenomena.

This means there is no need to find solutions outside of ourselves, merely to seek the faults within.

That is the role of the true practitioner.

Catherine writes too about the gut. That vast organ that is at the core of our health. It is so often dismissed and yet, now, even conventional medicine is beginning to realise its effects on the rest of the body. Gut health is fundamental to our overall wellbeing. And the understanding of dysfunction and the subsequent remedy utterly paramount to overall health. We talk of The National Health Service but it is more the National 'ill' Health Service! Giving remedies to change symptoms with complex chemicals, rather than addressing the more subtle attainment of 'Health'.

Add to this the effects that the mind has in influencing all of our functions. And you have the almost impossible task of finding the core of the problem and how to address it.

Catherine, with her chosen field of Integrated Chinese Medicine, taps in to all of these physiological fields. And weaves her special 'Practitionership Magic' in deciphering the diagnostic clues and produce the necessary remedy. This is where the skill lies. The need to interpret the signs, both proffered and hidden, to help an individual to recover their health. Health is always there, it is in attaining it that needs a very special catalyst to bring about the necessary changes from within. It requires great levels of understanding and knowledge to bring these changes to fruition.

Catherine brings about these subtle changes with great humility, care and deep understanding.

Her writing in this book will enable many to understand their own issues of mind, body and spirit and give them the realistic hope of repair. The bruising of the mind being as important of that of the body.

Despite her own adversities she never fails to smile from within and deliver a therapeutic tonic from her own presence.

I hope that this well thought out book, will get the audience it deserves and may be revered by all fortunate enough to read it. As with all words of wisdom, some may fall on stony ground and may not take root. I hope that, as I have, others too will be nurtured by the seeds she has sown and will see the benefits accrue.

Barrie Savory,

Osteopath and Back Specialist
69 Harley Street.
London.

Printed in Great Britain
by Amazon